REVISE EDEXCEL GCSE (9—1)
Physical Education
Level 1 / Level 2 Full Course (1PE0) & Short Course (3PE0)

REVISION WORKBOOK

Series Consultant: Harry Smith

Author: Jan Simister

Notes from the publisher

1. In order to ensure that this resource offers high-quality support for the associated Pearson qualification, it has been through a review process by the awarding body. This process confirms that this resource fully covers the teaching and learning content of the specification or part of a specification at which it is aimed. It also confirms that it demonstrates an appropriate balance between the development of subject skills, knowledge and understanding, in addition to preparation for assessment.

Endorsement does not cover any guidance on assessment activities or processes (e.g. practice questions or advice on how to answer assessment questions) included in the resource, nor does it prescribe any particular approach to the teaching or delivery of a related course.

While the publishers have made every attempt to ensure that advice on the qualification and its assessment is accurate, the official specification and associated assessment guidance materials are the only authoritative source of information and should always be referred to for definitive guidance.

Pearson examiners have not contributed to any sections in this resource relevant to examination papers for which they have responsibility.

Examiners will not use endorsed resources as a source of material for any assessment set by Pearson.

Endorsement of a resource does not mean that the resource is required to achieve this Pearson qualification, nor does it mean that it is the only suitable material available to support the qualification, and any resource lists produced by the awarding body shall include this and other appropriate resources.

2. Pearson has robust editorial processes, including answer and fact checks, to ensure the accuracy of the content in this publication, and every effort is made to ensure this publication is free of errors. We are, however, only human, and occasionally errors do occur. Pearson is not liable for any misunderstandings that arise as a result of errors in this publication, but it is our priority to ensure that the content is accurate. If you spot an error, please do contact us at resourcescorrections@pearson.com so we can make sure it is corrected.

For the full range of Pearson revision titles across KS2, KS3, GCSE, Functional Skills, AS/A Level and BTEC visit:

www.pearsonschools.co.uk/revise

Question difficulty

Look at this scale next to each exam-style question. It tells you how difficult the question is.

Contents

Students studying the full course need to study all topics and those studying the short course need to study the topics highlighted.

COMPONENT 1: FITNESS AND BODY SYSTEMS

Topic 1: Applied anatomy and physiology
1 Functions of the skeleton
2 Classification of bones
3 Structure of the skeleton
4 Classification of joints
5 Movement at joints 1
6 Movement at joints 2
7 Movement at joints 3
8 Ligaments, tendons and muscle types
9 Muscles
10 Antagonistic muscle pairs: biceps and triceps
11 Antagonistic muscle pairs: quadriceps and hamstrings
12 Antagonistic muscle pairs: gastrocnemius and tibialis anterior
13 Antagonistic muscle pairs: hip flexors and gluteus maximus
14 Muscle fibre types
15 Cardiovascular system 1
16 Cardiovascular system 2
17 Blood vessels
18 Vascular shunting
19 Plasma, platelets and blood cells
20 Composition of air
21 Lung volumes
22 The respiratory system
23 The alveoli and gas exchange
24 Energy and energy sources
25 Short-term effects of exercise on the muscular system
26 Short-term effects of exercise on the cardio-respiratory system

Topic 2: Movement analysis
27 Lever systems 1
28 Lever systems 2
29 Planes and axes of movement 1
30 Planes and axes of movement 2

Topic 3: Physical training
31 Fitness, health, exercise and performance
32 The relationship between health and fitness
33 Cardiovascular fitness
34 Muscular endurance
35 Flexibility
36 Reaction time
37 Power and speed
38 Agility
39 Balance and co-ordination
40 Body composition and strength
41 PARQ and fitness tests
42 Cardiovascular fitness tests
43 Strength and flexibility tests
44 Agility and speed tests
45 Power and muscular endurance tests
46 Interpreting fitness test results
47 Progressive overload
48 Specificity
49 Individual needs and overtraining
50 FITT and reversibility
51 Thresholds of training
52 Continuous training
53 Fartlek training
54 Circuit training
55 Interval training
56 Plyometric training
57 Weight/resistance training
58 Fitness classes
59 Training methods: pros and cons
60 The effects and benefits of exercise to the skeletal system
61 Adaptations to the muscular system
62 Adaptations to the cardiovascular system 1
63 Adaptations to the cardiovascular system 2
64 The effects and benefits of exercise to the respiratory system
65 Injury prevention 1
66 Injury prevention 2
67 Fractures
68 Concussion and dislocation
69 Injuries at joints and soft tissue
70 Soft tissue injuries and RICE
71 Anabolic steroids
72 Beta blockers
73 Diuretics
74 Narcotic analgesics
75 Peptide hormones
76 Stimulants
77 Blood doping
78 Warm up
79 Cool down
80 Component 1 – Extended answer question 1
81 Component 1 – Extended answer question 2

COMPONENT 2: HEALTH AND PERFORMANCE

Topic 1: Health, fitness and wellbeing
82 Improving health
83 Physical health
84 Emotional health
85 Social health
86 Lifestyle choices 1
87 Lifestyle choices 2
88 Sedentary lifestyle
89 Impact of a sedentary lifestyle on weight
90 Diet and energy balance
91 Macronutrients
92 Micronutrients
93 Optimum weight
94 Dietary manipulation

Topic 2: Sport psychology
95 Classification of skills 1
96 Classification of skills 2
97 Massed and distributed practice
98 Fixed and variable practice
99 Values of goal setting 1
100 Values of goal setting 2
101 Visual and verbal guidance
102 Manual and mechanical guidance
103 Types of feedback
104 Mental rehearsal

Topic 3: Socio-cultural influences
105 Socio-economic groups
106 Gender and age groups
107 Ethnicity and disability groups
108 Commercialisation, the media and sport
109 The advantages of commercialisation
110 The disadvantages of commercialisation
111 Sporting behaviour
112 Deviance in sport
113 Component 2 – Extended answer question 1
114 Component 2 – Extended answer question 2

EXAM SKILLS
115 Multiple choice questions
116 Short answer questions
117 Use of data questions
118 Extended answer questions 1
119 Extended answer questions 2
120 Timed test 1
128 Timed test 2
134 Answers

A small bit of small print

Edexcel publishes Sample Assessment Material and the Specification on its website. This is the official content and this book should be used in conjunction with it. The questions in 'Now try this' have been written to help you practise every topic in the book. Remember: the real exam questions may not look like this.

Functions of the skeleton

Guided

1 The skeleton has many functions.

(a) One of the functions of the skeleton is to provide protection. Give **two** examples from physical activity to explain how the skeleton provides protection.

The skull protects the brain if hit in the head by a hockey stick ....

....

....

....   **(4 marks)**

(b) In the table below, state **two** functions of the skeleton other than protection, and give an example of their use in physical activity.

Function of the skeleton	Example of use in physical activity

(4 marks)

2 For each image, identify a **different** role of the skeletal system and describe how the role is achieved in the image

Use the images to help you answer the question.

Figure 1 ....

....

....

....

Figure 1

Figure 2 ....

....

....

....

Figure 2

(4 marks)

3 Choose words from the box to complete the statement below.

muscles ligaments bones movement levers support

.... act as .... to provide

.... when contracting ....

(connected via a tendon) pull them.   **(4 marks)**

Classification of bones

1 Identify the type of bone shown in **Figure 1**.

> Give the type **not** name of the the bone. Look at the shape of the bone to help identify the type.

Figure 1

.... **(1 mark)**

2 Which of the following statements is correct?

☐ **A** The scapular is an irregular bone.

☐ **B** The ribs are short bones.

☐ **C** The cranium is a flat bone.

☐ **D** Short bones act as levers.

(1 mark)

3 Describe, using different examples, **two** functions of flat bones.

Guided

The sternum is a flat bone. It is used for protection, for example ....

....

.... **(4 marks)**

4 Figure 2 shows four different types of bones, labelled **A–D**.

(a) Identify the bone type in **Figure 2** that is designed for strength or weight bearing.

.... **(1 mark)**

(b) What is the classification name for this type of bone?

.... **(1 mark)**

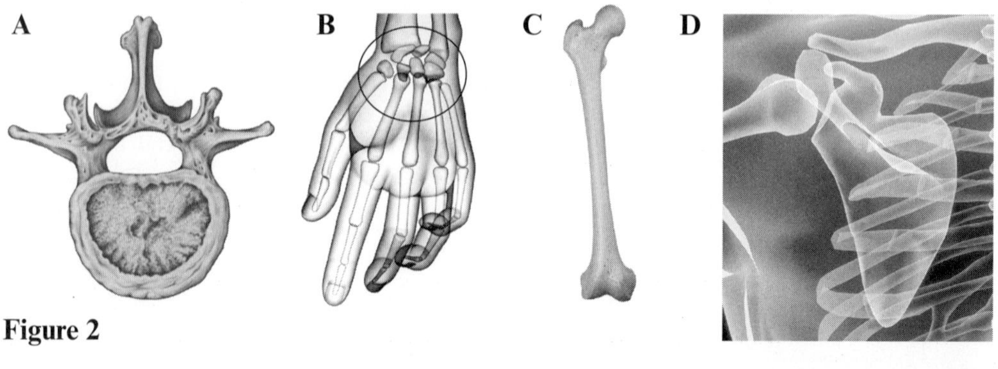

A   **B**   **C**   **D**

Figure 2

Structure of the skeleton

1 (a) Name the **two** bones located in the lower arm.

.... **(2 marks)**

(b) Name the bones that can be found in both the feet and the hands.

....

(1 mark)

> Read the question carefully: you need to think of the bones that are in **both** the feet **and** the hands, not two different bones.

2 Identify the two regions of the vertebral column labelled **B** and **D** in **Figure 1**.

B ....

D ....

(2 marks)

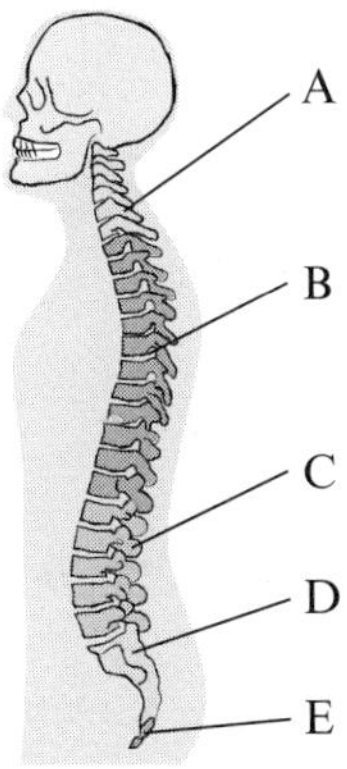

Figure 1

3 Identify the two bones labelled **A** and **B** in **Figure 2**. Use an example from physical activity to explain their function.

....

....

....

....

(4 marks)

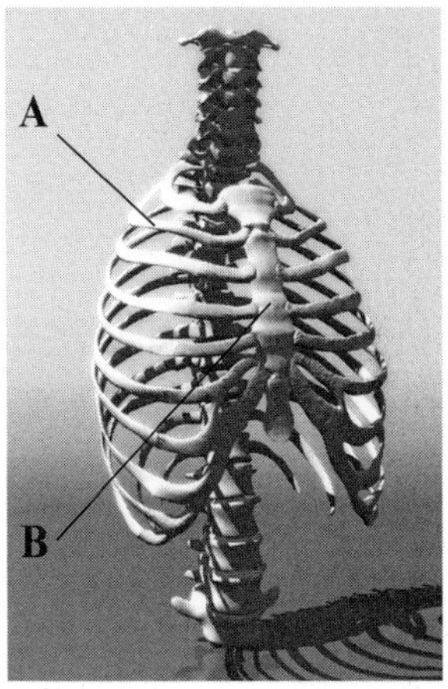

Figure 2

4 State the location of the femur and the name of one of the bones that it forms a joint with.

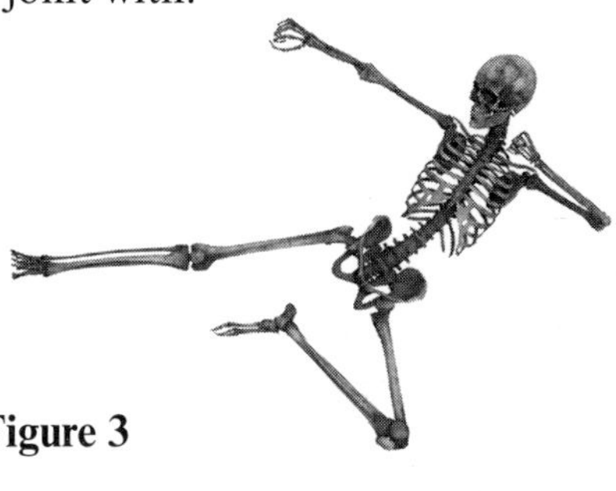

> **Guided**

Figure 3

The femur is located in the upper leg ....

....

....

.... **(2 marks)**

3

Had a go ☐   Nearly there ☐   Nailed it! ☐

Classification of joints

1 (a) Define the term **joint**.

.... **(1 mark)**

(b) For each of the images in **Figure 1**:
  • name the joint indicated by the arrow
  • state the **type** of joint indicated by the arrow.

> Look at the movements the athletes are performing to help you identify the joint type.

Figure 1

Joint A Name ....

Type ....

Joint B Name ....

Type .... **(4 marks)**

2 Which one of the following is an example of a condyloid joint?

☐ **A** neck

☐ **B** knee

☐ **C** wrist

☐ **D** ankle **(1 mark)**

3 Using an example from sport, describe the range of movement possible at a hinge joint.

Guided

The elbow is a hinge joint. The range of movement at a hinge joint is

flexion and ....

....

.... **(2 marks)**

Movement at joints 1

EXAM ALERT

1 (a) Describe the term **flexion** in relation to movement at a joint, and give an example from physical activity.

....

....

.... **(2 marks)**

> Make sure that any example you give is very clearly an example of the specific movement asked for. Kicking a football would be too vague.

(b) Describe the term **extension** in relation to movement at a joint, and give an example from physical activity.

....

.... **(2 marks)**

Guided

2 The following images show people participating in a range of physical activities.

(a) Circle all occasions in **Figure 1** and **Figure 2** where flexion is occurring and name the joint.

hip

Figure 1

Figure 2
(5 marks)

(b) Circle all occasions in **Figure 3** and **Figure 4** where extension is occurring and name the joint.

Figure 3

Figure 4
(5 marks)

Had a go ☐   Nearly there ☐   Nailed it! ☐

Movement at joints 2

1 (a) Describe the term **abduction** in relation to movement at a joint and give an example from physical activity.

....

.... **(2 marks)**

> **Guided**

(b) Describe the term **rotation** in relation to movement at a joint and give an example from physical activity.

Rotation is ...., for example

the .... action in cricket. **(2 marks)**

2 The following images show people participating in physical activities.

> Remember abduction means to take something away.

(a) Which of **Figure 1** or **Figure 2** shows abduction at the shoulder?

| Figure 1 | Figure 2 |

.... **(1 mark)**

(b) Which of the following is correct in identifying movement at the joints in **Figure 3** and **Figure 4**?

☐ **A** There is no rotation taking place in either image.

☐ **B** Abduction at the knee can be seen in Figure 4.

☐ **C** Both images show abduction of the arm at the shoulder.

☐ **D** The swimmer in Figure 3 is rotating the arm at the elbow. **(1 mark)**

| Figure 3 | Figure 4 |

Movement at joints 3

1   Identify the joint action in **Figure 1**.

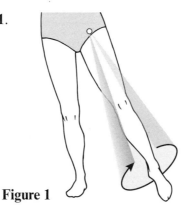

Notice the shape drawn by the leg and the arrow showing the movement. This should remind you which joint action moves in the shape of a cone.

Figure 1

.... **(1 mark)**

2   Describe the following terms and give an example for each from sport and physical activity.

(a) dorsi-flexion

....

.... **(2 marks)**

(b) plantar-flexion

....

.... **(2 marks)**

Guided

EXAM ALERT

3   **Figure 2** shows a footballer preparing to kick a ball. Analyse the joint actions occurring at each of the footballer's ankles.

Make sure you comment on all phases of the movement. Use the number of marks available as a guide to the amount you need to write.

Figure 2

.... is occurring at the ankle of the leg about to

kick the ball. This means that the toes are .... in

preparation to kick the ball. The action at the ankle next to the ball is

....

....

.... **(4 marks)**

Ligaments, tendons and muscle types

1 Name the type of tissue that connects the triceps to the ulna.

> First identify if the question is asking about two bones, two muscles, or one of each.

.... **(1 mark)**

2 Describe the role of the ligaments in sporting activity.

....

.... **(2 marks)**

3 Name the type of muscle located in the blood vessels.

.... **(1 mark)**

4 There are three different muscle types. Two of these types are said to contract unconsciously. Using an example, explain what is meant by **unconscious** muscle contraction.

....

.... **(2 marks)**

5 Identify the muscle type that forms the heart.

.... **(1 mark)**

6 Explain how tendons aid movement.

Guided

Tendons attach muscles to bone. This means that when the muscle ....

....

....

.... **(2 marks)**

Muscles

1 (a) Using the image of the squash player below, label the location of the pectoralis major and the external obliques.

(2 marks)

Guided

EXAM ALERT

(b) Analyse when the squash player will use each of these muscles during a game.

The player will need to turn their upper body to play

a backhand; they are able to rotate due to the action of the ....

| Always try to fully describe the movement so it is clear what you mean to someone reading it. |

....

....

....

(2 marks)

2 Draw lines to match **two** muscles to their correct role.

Deltoid   Rotates the trunk

Latissimus dorsi   Extends the leg at the hip

Pectoralis major   Flexes the arm at the elbow

External obliques   Abducts the arm at the shoulder   **(2 marks)**

3 Identify the muscle labelled **A** in **Figure 1** and explain its role.

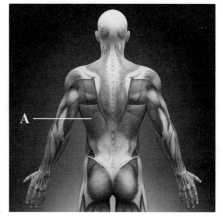

Figure 1

Muscle A is ....

The role of muscle A is ....

....   **(2 marks)**

Antagonistic muscle pairs: biceps and triceps

1 Name the muscle, at the front of the upper arm, identified as **A** in **Figure 1**.

Figure 1

.... **(1 mark)**

2 (a) Define the term **antagonistic muscle pairs**.

....

....

....

.... **(2 marks)**

(b) Name the muscle that works antagonistically with muscle **A** in **Figure 1**.

.... **(1 mark)**

(c) Analyse how these muscles act as an antagonistic pair.

Guided

When the biceps contract the triceps ....

This allows the runner to ....

....

.... **(2 marks)**

(d) Explain how the ability to use antagonistic pairs of muscles in his arms helps the sprinter in his performance.

....

.... **(2 marks)**

(e) Identify the range of movement at the elbow that results from the sprinter's arm muscles working antagonistically.

....

.... **(1 mark)**

Antagonistic muscle pairs: quadriceps and hamstrings

1 (a) (i) Name the muscle at the front of the thigh, identified as **B** in **Figure 1**.

Figure 1

.... **(1 mark)**

(ii) Identify the role of muscle **B**.

....

.... **(1 mark)**

(b) Give examples from three different sporting activities of how this muscle is used.

> Guided

One example is the follow through with the leg after taking a

shot at goal in football ....

....

....

....

.... **(3 marks)**

> Note the word **different** in the question: make sure all three examples are from different sports.

(c) (i) Name the muscle that works antagonistically with muscle **B** in **Figure 1**.

.... **(1 mark)**

(ii) Identify the role of this antagonistic muscle.

....

.... **(1 mark)**

(iii) Give an example of the use of this muscle, when acting as an agonist, in physical activity.

....

.... **(1 mark)**

Antagonistic muscle pairs: gastrocnemius and tibialis anterior

1 Analyse how the netballers in **Figure 1** are using the muscles in their lower leg to aid their performance.

....

....

....

....

(3 marks)

Figure 1

2 (a) Name the muscle located at the back of the lower leg.

....   **(1 mark)**

(b) Give examples from **three** different sporting activities of how this muscle is used in movement.

Guided

One example is pointing the toes when diving ....

....

....

....   **(3 marks)**

3 Analyse how the muscles in the lower leg enable the long jumper to execute the correct technique in **Figure 2**.

> Look at the shape of the foot. How do the muscles work together to produce this shape?

Figure 2

....

....

....

....   **(4 marks)**

Antagonistic muscle pairs: hip flexors and gluteus maximus

1 Identify the muscles labelled **A** and **B** in the **Figure 1** below.

A ....

B ....

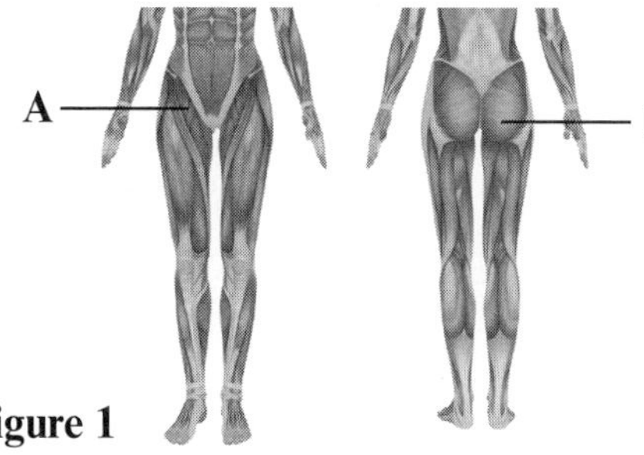

A —●   ●— B   (2 marks)

Figure 1

2 (a) Describe what is meant by extension at the hip.

....

.... (2 marks)

> Remember: if the question says **describe** you do not need to justify your answer.

(b) Name the agonist responsible for this action.

.... (1 mark)

(c) Give **one** example from physical activity where hip extension is required to execute a technique correctly.

.... (1 mark)

3 (a) Name the action occurring at the snowboarder's hip in **Figure 2**.

....

(1 mark)

(b) Name the agonist muscle responsible for the action.

....

(1 mark)

Figure 2

4 Analyse the muscle and joint action occurring at the hip as a football player takes their leg back and then brings it forward to kick the ball.

Guided ▷

The gluteus maximus is the agonist, taking the leg back to extend the

....

....

....

.... (4 marks)

Muscle fibre types

1 Identify the muscle fibre types that are being predominantly used in the two activities shown in **Figure 1** and **Figure 2**.

> Always read the question carefully. Check whether the question is referring to **types of muscle fibre** or d**i**fferent types of muscle.

Figure 1

Figure 2

Figure 1 ....

Figure 2 ....   **(2 marks)**

2 Identify a characteristic of **fast twitch type IIa** muscle fibres.

☐ **A** high capillary network

☐ **B** medium speed of contraction

☐ **C** high resistance to fatigue

☐ **D** low levels of mitochondria   **(1 mark)**

3 Complete the table below to show some of the characteristics of muscle fibre types.

	Slow twitch type I	Fast twitch type IIa	(a) ....
Force of contraction	low	(b)	very high
Resistance to fatigue	(c)	moderate	low

(3 marks)

4 Explain why having a greater number of fast twitch type IIx muscle fibres would be an advantage to a sprinter in a 100 m race.

Guided

Fast twitch type IIx muscles can contract the most ....

....

Therefore ....

....

....   **(3 marks)**

Cardiovascular system 1

1 Select the correct components of the cardiovascular system from the options below.

| Water | Heart | Lungs | Blood vessels | Blood | Brain |

> When given options, always go for the ones you definitely know are correct and eliminate the ones you definitely know are wrong first.

....   **(3 marks)**

2 (a) State **three** functions of the cardiovascular system.

(i) ....

(ii) ....

(iii) ....

(3 marks)

> Note the different command words. In (a) **state** requires you to simply state facts, whereas in (b) **explain** requires you to develop the point you are making using more detail (for example, by giving a function and then linking its relevance to physical activity).

(b) Explain the relevance of **one** of the functions of the cardiovascular system to physical activity.

....

....

....

(3 marks)

3 State what happens to the blood vessels under the surface of the skin to help maintain body heat when playing outside on a very cold day.

....   **(1 mark)**

4 Identify the by-product from energy production that is transported away from the working muscles via the cardiovascular system.

....   **(1 mark)**

5 Explain the role of the blood vessels in regulating body temperature when body heat increases during physical activity.

Guided

The blood vessels under the skin increase in

diameter. This is called ....

....

....

....

Figure 1

....   **(4 marks)**

15

Cardiovascular system 2

1 (a) Identify the parts of the heart labelled **A** and **B** in **Figure 1**.

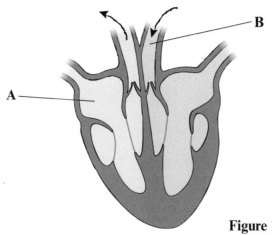

Figure 1

A ....

B ....   **(2 marks)**

(b) Describe the role of the part labelled **B**.

....

....   **(2 marks)**

2 Describe the location **and** role of the bicuspid valve in circulating blood for performance.

EXAM ALERT

....

....

....

....   **(3 marks)**

> Remember to use linking words such as **so that**, **therefore** and **this means** to show how what you know about a topic is relevant to performance.

3 Which **one** of the following accurately describes the location of the septum?

☐ **A** The septum surrounds the heart.

☐ **B** The septum separates the left and right sides of the heart.

☐ **C** The septum separates the left and right atrium.

☐ **D** The septum separates the left and right ventricle.   **(1 mark)**

4 Explain the role of the vena cava during performance in physical activity and sport.

> **Guided**

The vena cava is the main .... that transports

.... blood to the heart. The blood is ....

as the ....

....

....   **(4 marks)**

> What do you know about the vena cava? What do you know about the effects of exercise? Link the two together.

Blood vessels

1 Name the **three** different types of blood vessel.

(i) ....

(ii) ....

(iii) .... **(3 marks)**

2 Name the type of blood vessel that normally carries oxygenated blood.

.... **(1 mark)**

3 Explain why veins need valves to fulfil their function.

....

....

....

.... **(3 marks)**

Guided

4 Explain the role of capillaries in ensuring sufficient oxygen reaches the muscles for aerobic activity.

The role of the capillaries is to allow gaseous exchange

by taking ....

....

....

....

....

> Break down the question in to smaller parts. What do capillaries do? How does this make sure enough oxygen reaches the muscles? It will help you to think about the movement of oxygen from the lungs. Think about the alveoli in the lungs and the role of the capillaries around the alveoli and in the muscles.

(4 marks)

EXAM ALERT

5 Explain how **one** characteristic of an artery makes it suitable for its role.

....

....

....

....

....

> Look for the key words here: **explain** and **characteristic**. Use the number of marks as a guide to the number of points you should be making. This is a 4-mark question so will need to link four points.

(4 marks)

Vascular shunting

Guided

1   Using examples, describe what is meant by **vascular shunting**.

Vascular shunting is the term for the process when blood flow to

different parts of the body is altered depending on demand for oxygen.

For example, when exercising ....

....

.... **(3 marks)**

2   (a)   As demands on the body increase due to exercise, blood flow
to different parts of the body alters. Explain how vasodilation
and vasoconstriction allow redistribution of blood flow to the
digestive system during exercise.

> Use your knowledge of the words **constriction** and **dilation** to help, and remember **vaso** relates to blood vessels.

....

....

....

.... **(4 marks)**

(b)   Explain why vascular shunting is beneficial for the performer as long as they
have not eaten recently.

....

....

....

.... **(4 marks)**

3   Analyse the data in **Figure 1** and **Figure 2** to determine the changes in blood
flow as a result of exercise.

Use of data

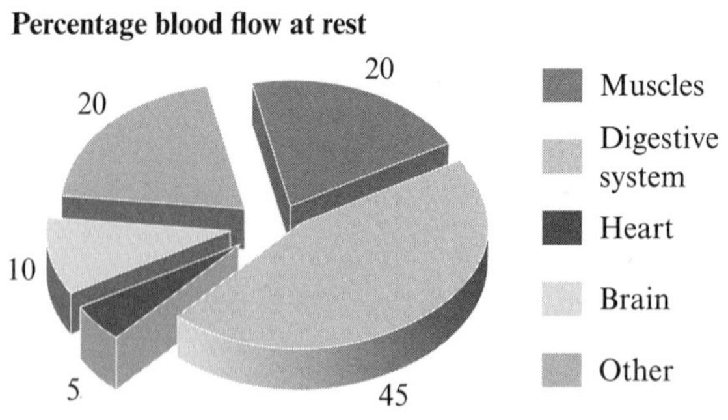

Percentage blood flow at rest

20   20   10   5   45

Muscles
Digestive system
Heart
Brain
Other

Percentage blood flow during exercise

5   5   5   5   80

Active muscles
Digestive system
Heart
Brain
Other

Figure 1 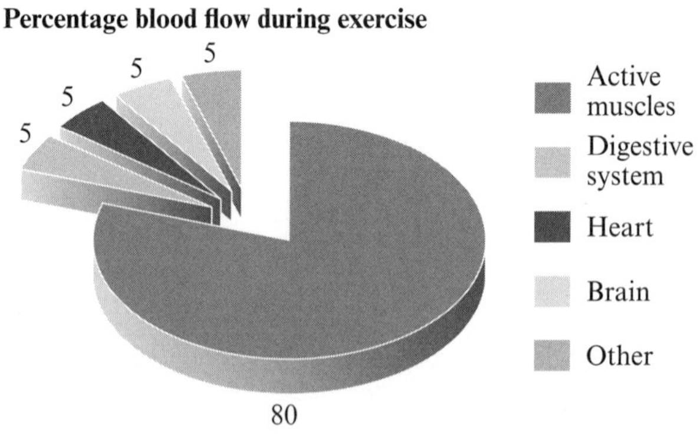   **Figure 2**

....

....

.... **(4 marks)**

Plasma, platelets and blood cells

1 Plasma is the liquid part of the blood. State the other components of the blood.

....

.... **(3 marks)**

Guided

2 Binna, JC and Squeak play rugby for the school rugby team. During a tackle Binna receives a cut to the head. Due to this open wound she has to leave the pitch. Explain the role of the blood in ensuring Binna's return to the game after a short break.

This is an **explain** question, so you will need to justify why Binna can return to the game.

....

.... **(3 marks)**

preventing further blood loss and preventing her from being a potential

risk to others.

3 Explain the importance of red blood cells to performance in long-distance running.

Think about the role of red blood cells and how this links to the length of this event.

....

....

....

....

....

.... **(4 marks)**

4 White blood cells fight infection. Explain how this is an advantage to an elite performer.

....

....

....

.... **(3 marks)**

Composition of air

EXAM ALERT

1 State the difference between the inhaled and exhaled air.

....

....

(1 mark)

> Although there is only one mark available for question 1, the question asks for the **difference between two things**, so you will need to address both to get the mark. It would not be enough to talk about just one.

2 Identify which of the diagrams in **Figure 1** correctly represents:

(i) the composition of inhaled air ....

(ii) the composition of exhaled air ....

(2 marks)

> Use the knowledge you have about the percentages to interpret the diagrams and find the correct ones.

Use of data

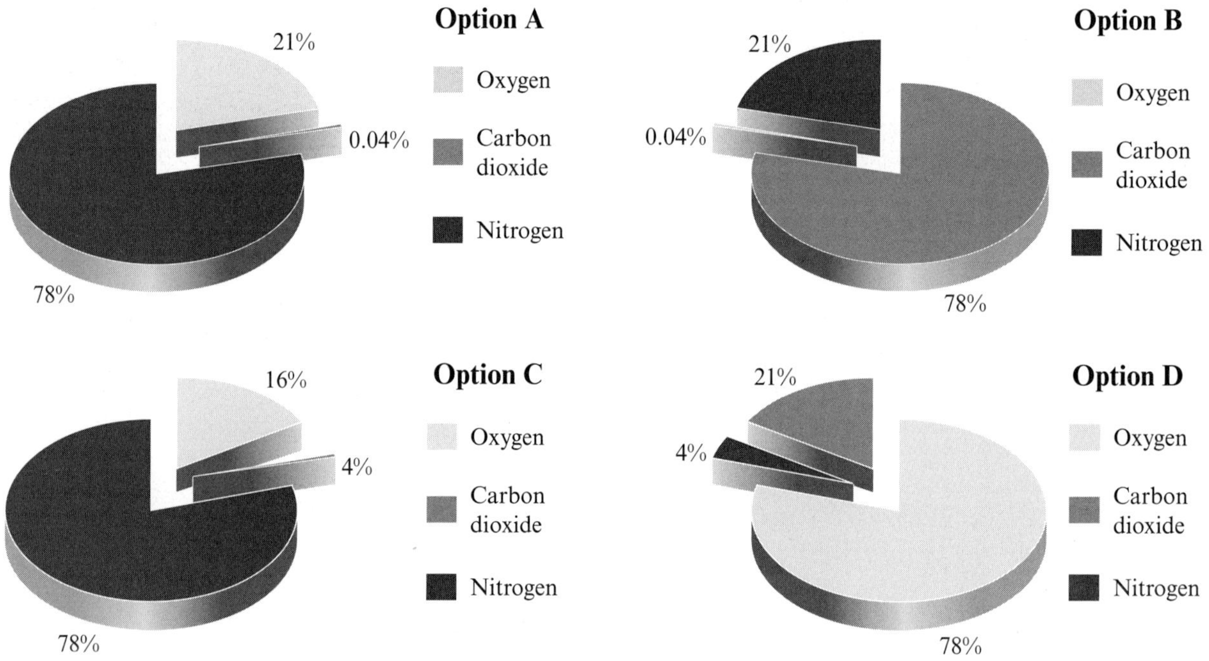

Option A
21%
0.04%
78%
Oxygen
Carbon dioxide
Nitrogen

Option B
21%
0.04%
78%
Oxygen
Carbon dioxide
Nitrogen

Option C
16%
4%
78%
Oxygen
Carbon dioxide
Nitrogen

Option D
21%
4%
78%
Oxygen
Carbon dioxide
Nitrogen

Figure 1

3 Explain why exhaled air has a different percentage of carbon dioxide than inhaled air.

Guided

Exhaled air has a .... percentage of carbon dioxide than

inhaled air, because ....

....

(3 marks)

4 Explain the impact of physical activity on oxygen levels in exhaled air compared to inhaled air.

....

....

....

(3 marks)

Lung volumes

1   Which **one** of the following is the correct term for normal breathing at rest?

☐ **A**   stroke volume   ☐ **C**   tidal volume

☐ **B**   vital capacity   ☐ **D**   cardiac output   **(1 mark)**

2   **Figure 1** shows players participating in a game of football. Explain the variations in tidal volume as the players change pace in the game.

> Think about what happens to your breathing when you start to run faster.

....

....

....

....

....

....

(4 marks)

Figure 1

3   **Figure 2** shows a performer's lung volumes at rest.

Guided

Use of data

(a)   Analyse **Figure 2** to determine the player's lung volumes at rest.

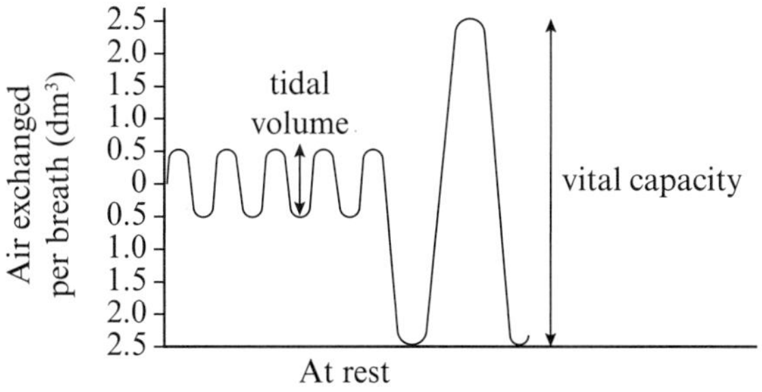

Figure 2

At rest, the tidal volume is ....

The vital capacity is ....   **(2 marks)**

(b)   Explain the expected changes to this graph if the player begins to exercise.

....

....

....

....

....

(4 marks)

The respiratory system

1 (a) Describe the roles of the diaphragm and the bronchioles in the movement of oxygen into the body.

Diaphragm ....

....

....

Bronchioles ....

....

....   **(4 marks)**

EXAM ALERT

(b) Identify the diaphragm and bronchioles on **Figure 1** by drawing a line and labelling them.

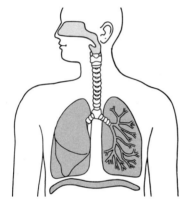

Figure 1

> If you are asked to add label lines to a diagram make sure it is very clear which part of the diagram the line is pointing to.

(2 marks)

(c) Using **Figure 1**, explain whether the diagram represents the respiratory system during inspiration or expiration.

....

....

....

....

....

> Generally when answering 'explain' questions you need to **show your knowledge** and either **apply or justify the point** you are making. Remember, if the question asks you to **explain** you need to include a **justification** or **reason** to support the initial point too.

(3 marks)

The alveoli and gas exchange

1 Identify which **one** of the following is part of the structure of alveoli.

☐ **A** muscular wall   ☐ **C** has valves

☐ **B** carried in the blood   ☐ **D** thin-walled   **(1 mark)**

2 Complete **Figure 1** by adding arrows to the diagram to represent the movement of gases between the tissue cells of the muscle and the capillaries.   **(2 marks)**

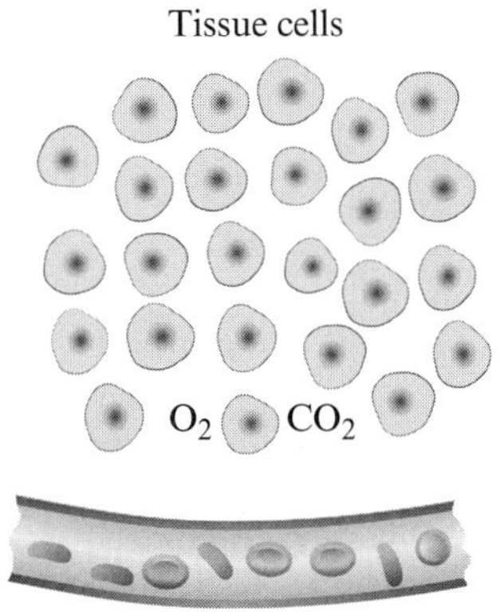

Tissue cells

O_2 CO_2

> Think about the location where gaseous exchange is taking place. What will the muscles be in short supply of during exercise?

Figure 1

3 Describe the process of gaseous exchange at the muscles.

....

....

....

....   **(4 marks)**

4 Using **Figure 2**, explain the movement of gases at the alveoli.

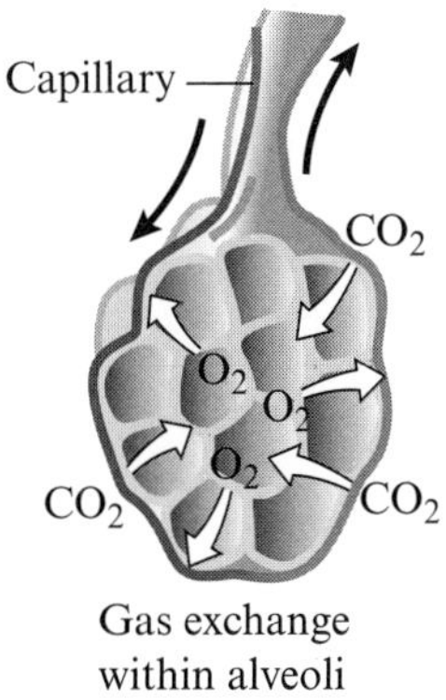

Guided

EXAM ALERT

Capillary

CO_2

O_2 O_2

CO_2 O_2 CO_2

Gas exchange within alveoli

Figure 2

> Check the command word used in a question. If it is **explain**, you must give a reason in your answer.

Capillaries around the alveoli contain blood with a low concentration of

oxygen and a high concentration of ....

....

....

....

....   **(4 marks)**

Energy and energy sources

1 State the energy source for anaerobic activity.

.... **(1 mark)**

2 Which **one** of the following performers would use anaerobic respiration to complete their activity or stated technique?

> You need to apply your knowledge to answer this question. Think about the duration of the activity or technique and the intensity of the action.

☐ **A** a marathon runner six miles into the race

☐ **B** a hockey goal keeper standing in goal

☐ **C** a tennis player serving an ace

☐ **D** a footballer jogging back into position **(1 mark)**

3 Which one of the following is a by-product of anaerobic respiration?

> Remember: anaerobic means without oxygen.

☐ **A** carbon dioxide

☐ **B** glucose

☐ **C** water

☐ **D** lactic acid **(1 mark)**

4 For a physical activity or sport of your choice, give an example of a specific technique or point in the activity where the performer would need to produce energy using (i) aerobic respiration and (ii) anaerobic respiration.

Physical activity/sport ....

(i) Point/technique where energy is produced using aerobic respiration

....

(ii) Point/technique where energy is produced using anaerobic respiration

.... **(2 marks)**

5 Describe the difference in energy production between aerobic and anaerobic respiration.

Guided

To respire aerobically the body needs glucose and oxygen, whereas

anaerobic respiration does not require oxygen. The two processes of

respiration produce different by-products: ....

....

....

.... **(4 marks)**

Short-term effects of exercise on the muscular system

1 State the meaning of the term **short-term effect of exercise**.

.... (1 mark)

2 Give an example of a short-term effect of exercise on the muscular system.

.... (1 mark)

3 Which one of the following is a short-term effect of exercise on the muscular system?

☐ **A** decrease in heart rate

☐ **B** increase in muscle strength

☐ **C** decrease in lactic acid production

☐ **D** increase in lactate (1 mark)

> Watch out for the key words in a question. In this question, key information is that it is **short-term** and the **muscular system.**

4 **Figure 1** shows a number of runners leaving their blocks just after the start of their race.

Explain **two** short-term effects of this type of exercise on the runners' muscular system.

Figure 1

....

....

....

....

.... (4 marks)

5 Explain why sports performers may reduce the intensity they are working at during a game.

> Guided

They may experience ....

....

This slows energy production, meaning that the muscles have to reduce

....

.... (4 marks)

Short-term effects of exercise on the cardio-respiratory system

EXAM ALERT

1 Which **one** of the following is a short-term effect of exercise on the cardio-respiratory system?

☐ **A** decrease in heart rate

☐ **B** increase in muscle strength

☐ **C** decrease in breathing rate

☐ **D** increase in blood pressure

(1 mark)

> Watch out for the key words in a question. In this question, key information is that it is **short-term** and the **cardio-respiratory system**.

EXAM ALERT

2 Describe **one** short-term effect of exercise on the cardio-respiratory system.

....

....

....

(3 marks)

> To gain three marks you will need to identify a short-term effect of exercise and make two further linked points that describe the short-term effect you have identified.

3 Explain why heart rate needs to increase as a result of exercise.

....

....

....

(3 marks)

Guided

4 The graph in **Figure 1** shows breathing rates at rest, during exercise and immediately after exercise.

Explain why the breathing rate is at the level it is after exercise.

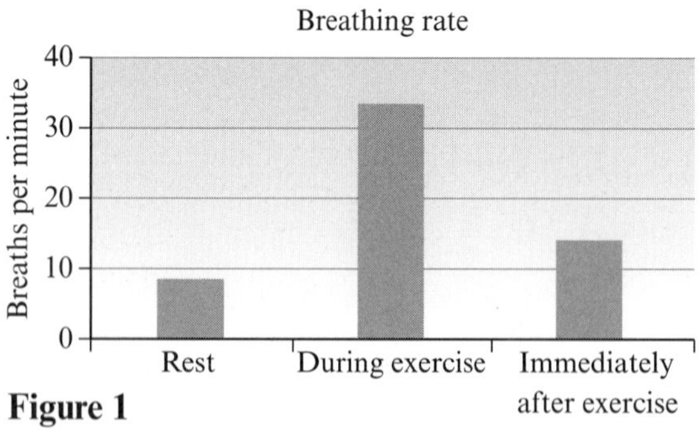

Use of data

Breathing rate

Figure 1

Figure 1 shows that the breathing rate immediately after exercise is higher than the resting breathing rate. This is because ....

....

....

....

(4 marks)

Lever systems 1

1 Which **one** of the following shows the correct symbols used to represent a lever system?

☐ A

☐ B

☐ C

☐ D

(1 mark)

> Guided

2 Complete the table by matching each part of the body to the relevant component of a lever system.

Parts of the body	Component of a lever system
Elbow joint	Fulcrum
Radius	
Weight of the hand	
Biceps	

(4 marks)

3 There are not many examples of first class lever systems in the body. State the component in the middle of a first class lever system.

.... (1 mark)

4 Give an example of a first class lever system in the body **and** its use in sport.

....

....

.... (2 marks)

5 **Figure 1** shows a performer at the start of a race. Identify, sketch and label the lever system operating at the ball of the foot during this sprint start.

> If asked to sketch a lever system, use the symbols you have learned. There is no need to make your sketch look like the runner.

Figure 1

(3 marks)

Lever systems 2

1 Third class lever systems are common in the body. State the component in the middle of a third class lever system.

.... **(1 mark)**

2 Give an example of a third class lever system in the body **and** its use in sport.

....

.... **(2 marks)**

3 State the mechanical advantage provided by a second class lever.

....

(1 mark)

> Remember this is looking for an advantage of a lever system, specifically a second class lever.

4 Explain the term **mechanical disadvantage** and use an example from sport to support your explanation.

....

....

....

.... **(3 marks)**

> This is an **explain** question, so make sure you give an example and justify your answer.

Guided

5 **Figure 1** shows a basketball player running past his opponent. Name, sketch and label the lever system operating at the knee during the running action.

This is a third class lever system.

Figure 1

(3 marks)

Planes and axes of movement 1

1 **Figure 1** shows the three planes in which movement can occur in the human body. Label the planes identified as **A** and **B**.

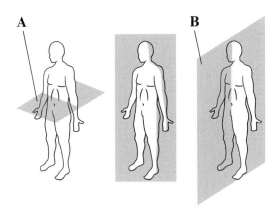

Figure 1

(2 marks)

2 State the name of the axis that allows movement in the transverse plane.

.... (1 mark)

3 Using an example, describe a plane of movement.

Guided

A plane is an imaginary line that shows the direction of movement

allowed in that plane. For example, ...

....

....

.... (3 marks)

4 State the direction of the movement allowed at the frontal plane.

....

(1 mark)

> Remember: movement can only follow the same direction as the plane.

5 Complete the table by matching each plane with its appropriate axis to allow movement.

Plane	Axis
Sagittal	
Frontal	
Transverse	

(3 marks)

Had a go ☐   Nearly there ☐   Nailed it! ☐

Planes and axes of movement 2

1 Which **one** of the following movements is allowed at the transverse plane?

☐ **A** flexion   ☐ **C** abduction

☐ **B** extension   ☐ **D** rotation   **(1 mark)**

> **Guided**

2 **Figure 1** shows two performers during an ice skating routine. Analyse **Figure 1** to determine the plane and axis of movement of the female ice skater as she completes the movement shown.

> When **analyse** is used with a picture, look carefully to see what the picture shows to help guide your answer.

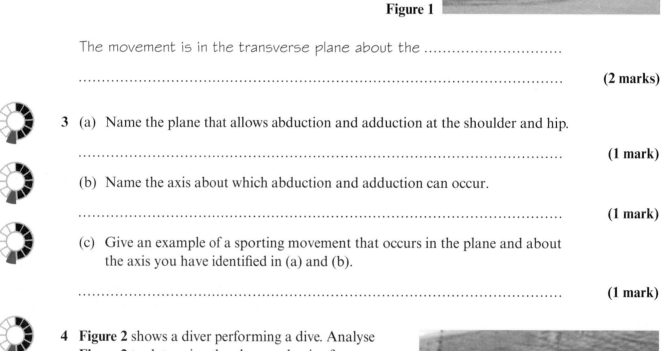

Figure 1

The movement is in the transverse plane about the ....

.... **(2 marks)**

3 (a) Name the plane that allows abduction and adduction at the shoulder and hip.

.... **(1 mark)**

(b) Name the axis about which abduction and adduction can occur.

.... **(1 mark)**

(c) Give an example of a sporting movement that occurs in the plane and about the axis you have identified in (a) and (b).

.... **(1 mark)**

4 **Figure 2** shows a diver performing a dive. Analyse **Figure 2** to determine the plane and axis of movement as the diver completes the movement shown.

....

....

....

....

(2 marks)

Figure 2

Fitness, health, exercise and performance

1 Define the terms **health** and **fitness**.

....

....

....

....

(2 marks)

> These terms are generally confused with one another. Ensure you learn the definition in the specification glossary.

EXAM ALERT

Short / Full

2 Using examples, explain what it means to be fit.

Fitness is ....

....

Different people will require different levels of fitness

depending on ....

....

....

....

....

....

....

(3 marks)

> Highlight the instructions in questions so that you don't forget them. For Question 2 you need to give examples and explain a term.

Guided

3 Define the term **performance**.

....

(1 mark)

4 Which **one** of the following states an advantage of exercise?

☐ **A** It is a good way of playing competitive sport.

☐ **B** It can cause injury.

☐ **C** It can cause muscle fatigue.

☐ **D** It can improve fitness.

(1 mark)

> Watch out for the key words in a question. In this question, the key word is **advantage**, so discount anything that is a disadvantage.

EXAM ALERT

The relationship between health and fitness

1 Complete the statements below about exercise and fitness.

(a) .... is a form of physical activity done to maintain or improve health. **(1 mark)**

(b) Performance should improve with an increase in .... **(1 mark)**

Short Full

(c) .... , fitness and exercise all contribute positively to create a balanced, healthy lifestyle. **(1 mark)**

2 **Figure 1** indicates a link between the four terms identified. Describe the link between these terms.

Guided

Short Full

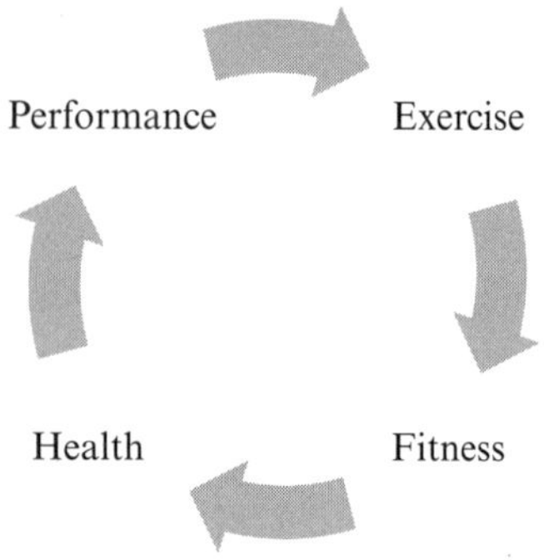

Performance → Exercise

Health ← Fitness

Figure 1

If you exercise regularly, you can increase your ....

....

....

....

....

....

....

.... **(4 marks)**

3 Explain how exercise links to performance in physical activity.

....

....

....

.... **(3 marks)**

Cardiovascular fitness

EXAM ALERT

1 In which **one** of the following events would the performers benefit most from high levels of cardiovascular fitness?

☐ **A**   100 m sprint

☐ **B**   400 m race

☐ **C**   triathlon

☐ **D**   gymnastics vault

> All of these performers could use cardiovascular fitness either during the activity or afterwards for recovery, so make sure you select the one where the benefit is the **greatest**.

(1 mark)

Guided

2 Complete the following statements about cardiovascular fitness.

(i) Cardiovascular fitness relies on the cardiovascular system supplying

sufficient .... to allow enough energy to be

released so that performers can continue to ....

for long periods of time without .... **(3 marks)**

Short / Full

(ii) A good level of cardiovascular fitness can reduce the chance of

suffering from .... as you get older. Therefore

cardiovascular fitness contributes to good physical health. **(1 mark)**

3 Long-distance cyclists need good muscular endurance to be successful in their event. Explain **one** other component of fitness that would be useful to a long-distance cyclist.

> For this question you need to:
> • identify an important component of fitness other than muscular endurance
> • state how it is useful for a long-distance cyclist.

....

....

....

(3 marks)

....

EXAM ALERT

4 Explain why cardiovascular fitness is more important than speed to a marathon runner.

> Make sure you clearly say why cardiovascular fitness is more important; it will not be enough to just state its importance.

....

....

....

....

(4 marks)

....

Muscular endurance

1 Taking part in regular exercise may improve muscular endurance. Which **one** of the following gives the best definition of muscular endurance?

☐ **A** the ability to exercise the entire body for long periods of time without tiring

☐ **B** the ability to exercise the heart and lungs and muscles in the body for long periods

☐ **C** the ability to exercise the muscles of the body for long periods of time without tiring

☐ **D** the ability to exercise the entire body for long periods of time   **(1 mark)**

2 Complete the following statements about muscular endurance.

> Guided

To have high levels of muscular endurance, the .... and

lungs must work together to supply sufficient .... to the

working muscles so that they can maintain the .... of the

work they are doing.   **(3 marks)**

3 Which **one** of the following statements is incorrect?

☐ **A** Long-distance runners require good cardiovascular fitness when they complete a sprint finish.

☐ **B** Games players are more likely to maintain the quality of their play throughout the match if they have excellent cardiovascular fitness.

☐ **C** Muscular endurance is vital in long-distance events such as the Tour de France cycle race.

☐ **D** Skaters need good muscular endurance to cover the 10 000 m in a long track race.   **(1 mark)**

4 Explain the importance of high levels of muscular endurance to the performance of a tennis player during a match.

> Guided

Muscular endurance is used for repeated muscle

contractions over a long period of time without

tiring. This means ....

....

....

....

(3 marks)

Flexibility

1 Define the term **flexibility**.

.... **(1 mark)**

2 Identify the **most appropriate** fitness test to measure flexibility.

☐ **A** vertical jump test

☐ **B** Harvard step test

☐ **C** sit and reach test

☐ **D** multi-stage fitness test **(1 mark)**

Guided

EXAM ALERT

3 Flexibility is an important component of fitness for many activities. Complete the table below to explain how each performer uses flexibility in their activity.

Performer	How flexibility is used in activity
Sprinter	Flexibility is used at the hip to get a long stride length and therefore use as few strides as possible to complete the race in a quicker time.
Javelin thrower	

> To achieve full marks, each response requires two parts. The first part should give an example of the use of flexibility and the second should extend the point by explaining how it will be an advantage to the performer. Make sure you make a link to the activity.

(4 marks)

EXAM ALERT

4 Explain the importance of flexibility at the hip to the following performers. Use a different explanation for each performer.

> Make sure your reasons are different to access both sets of marks.

(a) A gymnast in a floor routine

....

.... **(2 marks)**

(b) A hurdler during a race

....

.... **(2 marks)**

Reaction time

1   Using an example from a sport of your choice, describe what is meant by the term **reaction time**.

....

....   **(2 marks)**

> Do not repeat the question word. Instead use an alternative to **react**, for example **respond**.

2   Place in order the importance of reaction time to performers in the following activities and justify your order.

- Midfielder in a team game
- Gymnast completing a floor routine
- 100-metre sprinter

> Reaction time could be used by any of the performers, so think carefully about which performer needs it the most.

	Order of importance	Justification
1		
2		
3		

(6 marks)

3   **Figure 1** shows a goalkeeper diving for the ball. Using **Figure 1**, explain the importance of reaction time to the goalkeeper.

Guided

EXAM ALERT

> Sometimes it is helpful to start your answer by stating what the term means, then apply this knowledge to the question context.

Figure 1

The goalkeeper will need good reaction time when a shot has been

deflected off a defender. This is because ....

....

....   **(3 marks)**

Power and speed

1 Identify the component of fitness being described:

The rate at which an individual is able to perform a movement or cover a distance in a period of time.

.... **(1 mark)**

Guided

2 In the table, describe how each performer uses speed and what its effect is on performance. **(6 marks)**

Performer	Example of use of speed by performer in activity	Effect of speed on performance
Rugby player	To sprint past opponents with the ball	
Sprinter		To run faster and beat opponents
Long jumper		

3 Explain the use of power for **both** the javelin thrower **and** the tennis player.

Remember to link power specifically to each performer.

(4 marks)

Javelin thrower: ....

....

....

Tennis player: ....

....

....

Agility

1 Which **one** of the following components of fitness is the most important for a goalkeeper diving to save a deflected shot?

> If the answer you expect is not given in the options, choose the next best answer.

☐   **A**   agility

☐   **B**   power

☐   **C**   strength

☐   **D**   body composition

(1 mark)

2 Give examples to demonstrate the importance of agility in **two** different sporting activities.

Guided

Squash players need agility to change direction quickly to reach the

ball. Footballers need to use ....

....

(2 marks)

3 Discuss why agility is more important to a football player than to a 100 m sprinter.

....

....

....

....

(4 marks)

4 Complete the table by explaining how each performer uses agility in their activity.

Activity	Table tennis	Gymnastics
How the performer uses agility		

(4 marks)

Balance and co-ordination

EXAM ALERT

1 Which of the following components of fitness is the most important in the yoga pose shown in **Figure 1**?

> If an exam question talks about or shows a picture of a specific activity, you will need to apply your answer to this activity. Remember to select the most important.

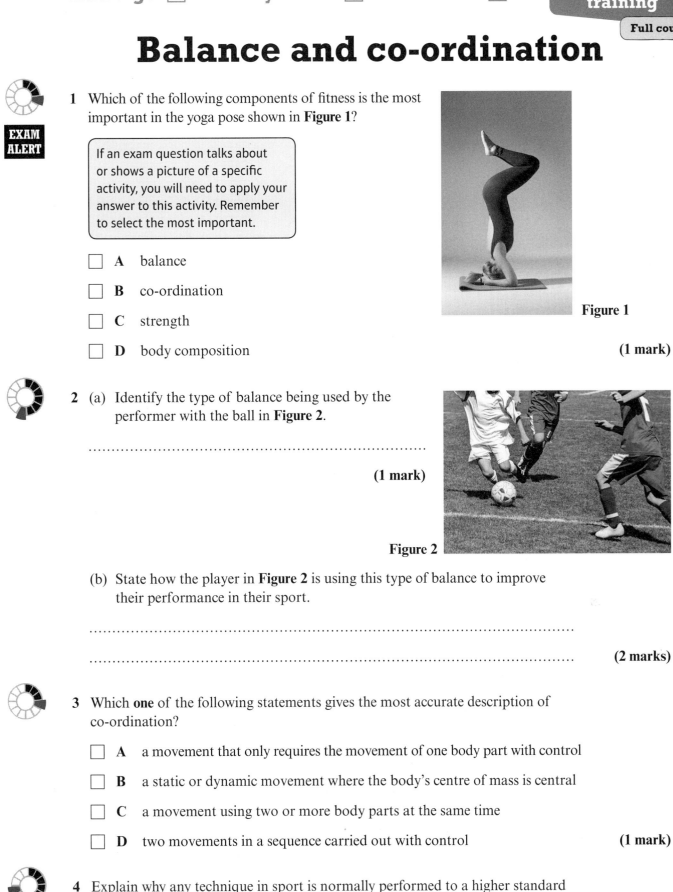

Figure 1

  ☐ **A**   balance

  ☐ **B**   co-ordination

  ☐ **C**   strength

  ☐ **D**   body composition

(1 mark)

2 (a) Identify the type of balance being used by the performer with the ball in **Figure 2**.

....

(1 mark)

Figure 2

(b) State how the player in **Figure 2** is using this type of balance to improve their performance in their sport.

....

....

(2 marks)

3 Which **one** of the following statements gives the most accurate description of co-ordination?

  ☐ **A**   a movement that only requires the movement of one body part with control

  ☐ **B**   a static or dynamic movement where the body's centre of mass is central

  ☐ **C**   a movement using two or more body parts at the same time

  ☐ **D**   two movements in a sequence carried out with control

(1 mark)

4 Explain why any technique in sport is normally performed to a higher standard if it is performed with a high level of co-ordination.

A co-ordinated movement will be efficient, smooth and therefore ....

....

....

....

(3 marks)

Guided

39

Body composition and strength

1 (a) **Figure 1** and **Figure 2** show two performers. Read the statements and decide which is true.

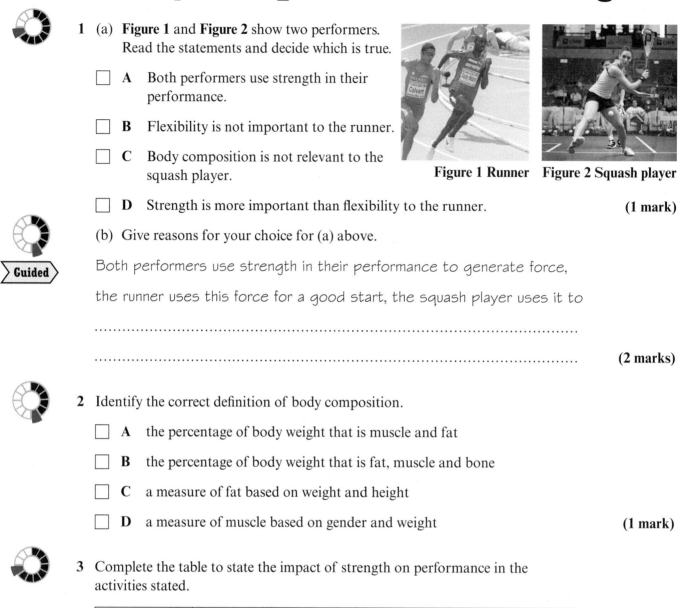

☐ **A** Both performers use strength in their performance.

☐ **B** Flexibility is not important to the runner.

☐ **C** Body composition is not relevant to the squash player.

Figure 1 Runner   Figure 2 Squash player

☐ **D** Strength is more important than flexibility to the runner.   **(1 mark)**

(b) Give reasons for your choice for (a) above.

> **Guided**

Both performers use strength in their performance to generate force,

the runner uses this force for a good start, the squash player uses it to

....

....   **(2 marks)**

2 Identify the correct definition of body composition.

☐ **A** the percentage of body weight that is muscle and fat

☐ **B** the percentage of body weight that is fat, muscle and bone

☐ **C** a measure of fat based on weight and height

☐ **D** a measure of muscle based on gender and weight   **(1 mark)**

3 Complete the table to state the impact of strength on performance in the activities stated.

Who needs it?	Why is it important?	What is the impact of strength on performance?
Weightlifter	To lift heavy weights	
Gymnast	To support own body weight	
Rock climber	To be able to hold own body weight	

(3 marks)

4 Briefly explain why strength is important to the player on the left of the picture in **Figure 3**.

EXAM ALERT

....

....   **(2 marks)**

> Use the command word, mark total and amount of space provided as a guide to how much you should write.

Figure 3 Football player

PARQ and fitness tests

1 Complete the PARQ shown below by adding two more typical questions that would normally be asked before allowing someone to take part in physical activity.

> What health and lifestyle issues might you need to know about before deciding if someone should exercise, or how much they should do?

PARQ

Name: Kam Kaur

Address: 21 Upper Street   London

_____

Personal dimensions (weight; height; sex):

57 kg, 1.67 m, female

1. Do you currently smoke? Yes / No

2. Do you drink more than recommended maximum units of alcohol per week?   Yes / No

3. Do you exercise on a regular basis (at least 3 times a week)?   Yes / No

4. Have you ever felt pain in your chest when you do physical exercise?   Yes / No

5. ....

6. ....

7. Do you know of any other reason why you should not participate in a programme of physical activity?   Yes / No

---

(2 marks)

2 State **two** reasons for completing a PARQ before starting a training programme.

....

.... **(2 marks)**

3 Fitness tests can be used to identify strengths and weakness in fitness. Give **one** other reason why fitness testing is of value.

.... **(1 mark)**

4 Michael plays rugby. The table below shows the ratings from Michael's first and latest set of fitness tests.

> Guided

If you were Michael's coach, explain how you could use these ratings to improve Michael's training programme so that all components of fitness are improved.

> Use of data

Fitness test	First	Last
Vertical jump	Average	Good
Sit and reach	Below average	Below average
30 m sprint	Average	Good

As Michael's coach I could look for the area that needs improving based

on the ratings. ....

....

.... **(3 marks)**

Cardiovascular fitness tests

1 Which **one** of the following is a test of cardiovascular fitness?

☐ **A**   vertical jump test

☐ **B**   sit and reach test

☐ **C**   30-metre sprint test

☐ **D**   Harvard step test   **(1 mark)**

2 Describe the test protocol for the Cooper 12-minute swim test.

> Guided

EXAM ALERT

To complete the Cooper 12-minute swim test, you need to

work with a partner: one swims, and one counts the number

of lengths. ....

Remember that **test protocol** means how the test is carried out. Use the number of marks available as a guide to how many points you need to make.

....

....

....

....   **(4 marks)**

3 (a) Give an example of a performer who would use the Harvard step test to
measure their fitness for their sport, stating why this would be an appropriate
test for them.

....

....

....   **(2 marks)**

(b) State why performers should test their fitness at the start and then again at
the end of their training programme.

....   **(1 mark)**

4 Elad and Stuart play water polo. Before starting a training programme they take
part in several fitness tests.

(a) Identify the most appropriate fitness test to measure the boys'
cardiovascular fitness.

....   **(1 mark)**

(b) Give a reason for selecting this test.

....   **(1 mark)**

....

....

Strength and flexibility tests

1 (a) Identify the tests shown in **Figure 1** and **Figure 2**.

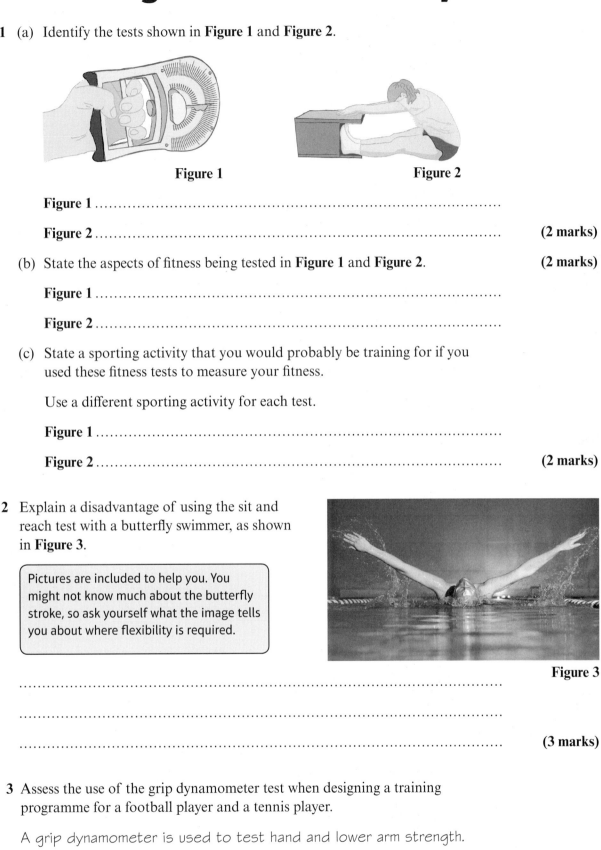

Figure 1   **Figure 2**

Figure 1 ....

Figure 2 .... **(2 marks)**

(b) State the aspects of fitness being tested in **Figure 1** and **Figure 2**. **(2 marks)**

Figure 1 ....

Figure 2 ....

(c) State a sporting activity that you would probably be training for if you used these fitness tests to measure your fitness.

Use a different sporting activity for each test.

Figure 1 ....

Figure 2 .... **(2 marks)**

2 Explain a disadvantage of using the sit and reach test with a butterfly swimmer, as shown in **Figure 3**.

> Pictures are included to help you. You might not know much about the butterfly stroke, so ask yourself what the image tells you about where flexibility is required.

Figure 3

....

....

.... **(3 marks)**

3 Assess the use of the grip dynamometer test when designing a training programme for a football player and a tennis player.

A grip dynamometer is used to test hand and lower arm strength.

Although both activities use strength this test is more relevant to the

....

.... **(4 marks)**

Agility and speed tests

1 (a) Identify one way in which the 30-metre sprint test is different from the Illinois agility test.

....

.... **(1 mark)**

> Think about the difference between speed and agility and therefore the different test designs.

(b) Explain how this variation makes the tests more relevant for their particular use.

....

....

....

.... **(2 marks)**

(c) (i) State two different activities that would be suitable for an individual who achieved an 'excellent' rating in the 30-metre sprint test.

....

.... **(2 marks)**

(ii) For each of these activities state how speed would be an advantage.

.... : speed over a short distance is really helpful

to beat your opponent to the ....

....

....

.... **(2 marks)**

2 (a) Identify the fitness test shown in **Figure 1**.

....

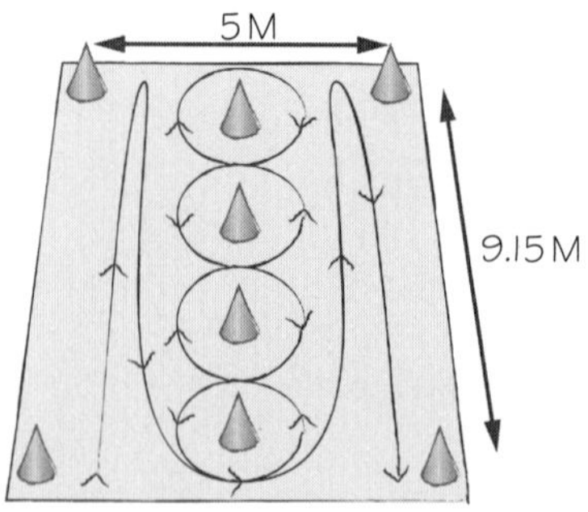

5 M

9.15 M

Figure 1

(1 mark)

(b) State an activity where the performers would find the results of this test useful.

.... **(1 mark)**

Power and muscular endurance tests

1   Carolyn would like to improve her volleyball performance. She has noticed that her arms get tired in the second half of a game and she would also like to jump higher so she can block the ball more easily.

Carolyn designs a training programme to improve her performance and has selected some fitness tests that she will complete at the beginning and the end of a training programme.

(a)   If Carolyn already knows what her areas for improvement are, give a reason why she should still complete fitness testing.

.... **(1 mark)**

(b)   Identify the fitness test being completed by Carolyn in **Figure 1**.

Figure 1

.... **(1 mark)**

(c)   State why Carolyn's choice of fitness test is appropriate.

Guided

Because it tests .... which is needed as she will use

repeated muscle contractions during her match. It also focuses on ......

....

....

.... **(2 marks)**

(d)   Based on the areas that Carolyn has identified as needing improvement:

    (i)   identify another fitness test that would be appropriate for Carolyn before she starts her programme

    Fitness test: ....

    (ii)   state the component of fitness that it tests.

    Component of fitness being tested: .... **(2 marks)**

Interpreting fitness test results

Mason plays rugby for the school team. He designed his personal exercise programme (PEP) around improving his fitness for rugby. Mason completed fitness tests before he started his training programme and also once a week throughout training to monitor his progress.

Summary of Mason's fitness test results

Test/rating	Before PEP	During PEP				After PEP
	4 Sept	11 Sept	18 Sept	25 Sept	2 Oct	9 Oct
One-minute sit-up	32	34	35	37	38	38
Rating	below average					
Vertical jump test	48	49	50	54	58	
Rating	average	average	good	good	good	excellent
Harvard step test	76	78		85	87	
Rating	average	average		above average	above average	

One-minute sit-up test normative data

Rating	Number of reps
Excellent	>49
Good	43–48
Above average	39–42
Average	35–38
Below average	31–34
Poor	<30

Vertical jump test normative data

Rating	cm
Excellent	>60
Good	50–60
Average	40–49
Fair	30–39
Poor	<30

Harvard step test normative data

Rating	Fitness index
Excellent	>90
Above average	80–89
Average	65–79
Below average	55–64
Poor	<55

1 (a) Using the normative data tables, complete the ratings for the one-minute sit-up test.

(1 mark)

(b) Identify the score Mason must have achieved to get an excellent rating for the vertical jump test.

.... **(1 mark)**

Maths skills

(c) Mason stepped for the full five minutes each time he took the Harvard step test.

(i) Calculate Mason's missing results when his heart rates were:

18 Sept: 130, 125, 120 ....

9 Oct: 120, 110, 100 ....

> Mason completed the full five minutes, which is 300 seconds. Use the following to calculate your answer: 100 × 300(s) divided by the total of the three heart rates.

> Round up scores over .5 and round down scores below .5 to the nearest whole number.

(2 marks)

(ii) Using Mason's Harvard step test scores from (c) (i), identify his ratings for this test and add them to the table.

(2 marks)

Guided

(d) Analyse Mason's one-minute sit-up test results.

Mason started below average and after six weeks ....

....

46 .... **(3 marks)**

Progressive overload

1 (a) Explain how you could tell if progressive overload was being applied in a training programme. **(3 marks)**

....

....

....

....

....

....

Guided

(b) Explain how you could tell if progressive overload had been successfully applied in a training programme by looking at an individual's fitness test results. **(4 marks)**

If I looked at the results of the first set of tests and compared these

to the second, I would see an ....

....

....

....

....

....

2 Identify the statement that shows the principle of progressive overload is being applied.

☐ **A** I trained for a few weeks before increasing the amount I lifted and I was careful to only increase it slowly so that I didn't get injured.

☐ **B** A friend of mine waited a week before they increased the workload, then they went from 15 kg to 30 kg in one go.

☐ **C** After the injury I couldn't workout at all for 4 weeks.

☐ **D** The following list shows the amounts I lifted on a week-by-week basis: 5 kg; 6 kg; 7 kg; 8 kg; 7 kg. **(1 mark)**

3 Explain whether you should apply the principle of overtraining or progressive overload to your training programme.

> Think carefully about the two terms. One principle means doing too much training, the other means gradually increasing the amount of training.

....

....

....

....

.... **(4 marks)**

Specificity

1 Identify the correct description of the principle of training specificity.

   ☐ A   matching training to the particular requirements of an activity

   ☐ B   matching the training to the requirements of the individual person

   ☐ C   matching the training to the requirements of the group

   ☐ D   matching the training to the requirements of the coach   **(1 mark)**

Guided

2 The performers listed below all apply the principles of training to their training programmes. State the training method these performers would be **most** likely to use if applying the principle of specificity to their training.

   (a) 100 m sprinter

   Interval training ....

   (b) Long-distance runner

   ....

   (c) Shot putter

   ....

   (d) Games player

   ....   **(4 marks)**

3 Two GCSE PE students were using fartlek training to improve their performance in their activities. One of the students played football; the other was a cross-country runner. Describe how each would adapt their use of this training method to follow the principle of specificity.

> Think about the different requirements for each activity and how fartlek training could be adapted to reflect the specific activity.

....

....

....

....

....

....

....

....   **(4 marks)**

Diuretics

1 One possible side effect of taking diuretics is dehydration.

(a) Briefly explain why dehydration can occur if a performer takes diuretics.

Because you are flushing all the liquid out of your body meaning you have no water inside your body as you are constantly peeing it out.

"more lost from the body than taken in"

(2 marks)

(b) Identify **two** other side effects from taking diuretics and explain why they are disadvantages for the performer.

kidney damage: they will be in hospital unable to perform ②

nauseous • distracted
• not completing tasks efficiently
• not completing a correct tackle
✓ learn!! ②

(4 marks)

(c) Identify **two** activities where performers might take a diuretic before their performance and explain why taking the diuretic gives them an advantage.

> Think about two different reasons why people take this category of drug – this should help you choose the different activities.

Horse racing – a jockey may take a diuretic to help *them lose weight to meet weight limit.*

sprinting to make use of other periods

> Don't just state the activities. Think about the benefits of diuretics and then think who would gain from these benefits.

(4 marks)

Narcotic analgesics

1 (a) Identify **two** possible harmful side effects from taking narcotic analgesics.

☑ vomiting

☐ insomnia

☐ acne

☐ slow heart rate

☐ facial hair in women

☐ loss of concentration

☐ heart failure

☑ kidney damage

☐ tiredness

(2 marks)

> Only tick the number of answers asked for in the question. If you tick more than you are asked for it is likely that none of your answers will count.

(b) State **one** way in which one of the side effects you selected in (a) could be potentially harmful to health.

If they are vomiting constantly then they will (be unable to perform) become dehydrated

※ vomiting ⟶ dehydration

(1 mark)

2 (a) Explain why a performer in an event of your choice might take narcotic analgesics.

> **Guided**

A tennis player may take narcotic analgesics after they have injured their muscles in their legs so they can continue playing and training even with injury so they can play in their next game

(2 marks)

(b) Explain why narcotic analgesics are banned.

Encourages a person to train with injuries meaning it could lead them to further damage.

> Think about your answer. You are not specifically asked why performers are tempted to take these drugs – but if you know the reason for that, it will help you think about why they are banned.

(2 marks)

Peptide hormones

Guided

1 Erythropoietin (EPO) is an example of a peptide hormone. Explain why a long-distance runner would be **more** tempted to take EPO than a sprinter.

EPO is more likely to be taken by a long-distance runner because it

increases *the O₂ to their working muscles so they can work harder for longer without fatiguing. Sprinters do not need their O₂ to their muscles as their race is only a few seconds.*

Having EPO allows me long distance athlete to maintain a good place in the competition

(4 marks)

EXAM ALERT

2 This is a list of possible harmful side effects from taking performance-enhancing drugs. Tick **two** that relate to the peptide hormone erythropoietin (EPO).

☐ dehydration

☐ insomnia

☐ acne

☐ slow heart rate

☐ facial hair in women

☐ loss of concentration

☒ heart failure

☒ increased viscosity of the blood

☐ tiredness

☐ masks injury

☐ nausea and vomiting

> Don't tick more answers than you are asked for in the question. If you do, it is likely that none of your answers will count.

(2 marks)

3 (a) State **two** reasons why a performer in an activity of your choice would take human growth hormones (HGH).

sprinter as they need increased muscle mass so have more powerful start and can maintain good stride. Burn more fat

(2 marks)

(b) An athlete would be banned if found taking HGH. Give **two** other disadvantages to a competitive athlete.

heart failure

abnormal growth in feet + hands

(2 marks)

Stimulants

1 (a) Explain **two** health risks associated with taking stimulants.

> Guided

Stimulants can cause increased anxiety, which can lead to ....

....

....

....

....

....

.... **(4 marks)**

(b) Explain **one** risk, other than to the performer's health, of taking stimulants.

> Read the question carefully. This asks for non-health risks. Make sure you do not give a health risk as your answer.

....

....

....

....

....

....

....

....

.... **(3 marks)**

2 Performers who test positive for stimulants will be disqualified from competition. Explain why boxers might be tempted to take them despite this risk.

....

....

....

....

....

....

....

.... **(3 marks)**

Blood doping

1 Which **one** of the following is a potential side effect of blood doping?

☐ **A** aggression

☐ **B** nausea

☐ **C** weight gain

☐ **D** infection **(1 mark)**

2 Which **one** of the following performers is **most** likely to be tempted to use blood doping?

☐ **A** sprinter

☐ **B** shot putter

☐ **C** archer

☐ **D** long-distance cyclist **(1 mark)**

3 Explain **one** risk associated with blood doping.

....

....

.... **(3 marks)**

4 Describe the method of blood doping.

Guided

Blood doping is where a performer has blood ....

and stored, so the body ....

....

.... **(3 marks)**

5 State why blood doping is a method rather than a performance-enhancing drug.

....

.... **(2 marks)**

6 Explain why a 400 m sprinter is unlikely to use blood doping to enhance their performance in their event.

Check the command words used in a question. If it is **explain** you need to give a reason in your answer, but if it is **describe** you do not. However, in both cases you must link the points you are making in your answer.

....

....

....

.... **(3 marks)**

Warm up

Guided

1 (a) Warm ups should be conducted before taking part in any form of physical activity.

Complete the table below.

- State, in the correct order, the three phases of a warm up.
- Give an example of a typical activity associated with that phase of the warm up.

Phase of warm up	Example activity
Pulse raiser	

(6 marks)

(b) Using examples, explain why the final phase of the warm up would vary, depending on the activity the performer was about to take part in.

....

....

....

....

....

.... (3 marks)

EXAM
ALERT

(c) Give **two** physical reasons why players should warm up before playing sport.

....

....

....

....

....

....

> The advice is usually to give different examples or reasons, but this question is asking specifically for **two physical** reasons.
>
> Make sure you read the question carefully and highlight the key words in the question.

(2 marks)

Cool down

1   Luke is taking part in a football training session.

(a)   After the main session, what should Luke ensure he does before the end of the training session?

.... **(1 mark)**

(b)   Using suitable examples, describe the phases of this part of the training session.

....

....

....

....

....

....

....

.... **(4 marks)**

(c)   State what will happen to the intensity of exercise during this final stage of the training session.

.... **(1 mark)**

(d)   Give four reasons why it is important that Luke carries out these activities at the end of his training session.

> Guided

> EXAM ALERT

To slowly return the body to its resting state and ....

....

....

....

....

....

....

....

.... **(4 marks)**

> Always read the question and make sure that you give the number of reasons you've been asked for in the question.

Had a go ☐ Nearly there ☐ Nailed it! ☐

Component 1 – Extended answer question 1

Guided

EXAM ALERT

Regular physical activity and training has an impact on the growth and development of the body systems. **Figure 1** shows the skeletal system of two basketball players.

Discuss the impact of training on the players' musculo-skeletal system and the potential impact of this on performance.

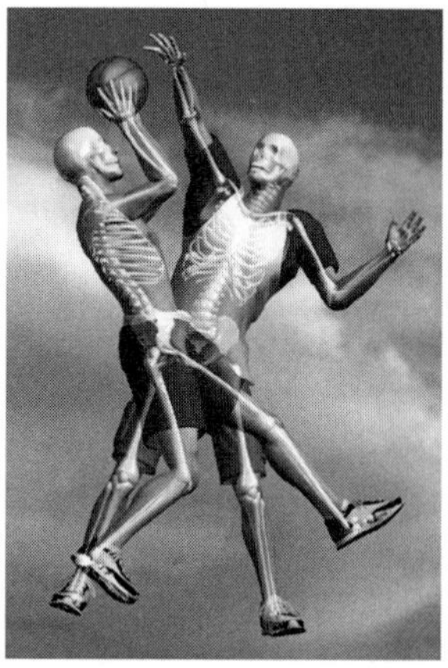

Figure 1

Remember that for extended answer questions you need to link your points together and use examples to support your statements.

....

While these effects are positive, if a performer trains too much this can cause ....

(9 marks)

Component 1 – Extended answer question 2

Guided

EXAM ALERT

Mrs Rana is coaching the school netball team and has designed a circuit training programme for the team to follow.

Evaluate whether circuit training would be the most appropriate choice of training method for the netball team.

Remember that for extended answer questions you need to link your points together and use examples to support your statements.

Circuit training is a flexible method of training that you can use to develop

skill and fitness, as you can have different activities at each ....

....

....

....

....

....

....

....

....

....

....

....

....

....

....

....

....

....

....

....

....

....

....   **(9 marks)**

Improving health

1 Which **one** of the following gives the most complete definition of health?

☐ **A** ability to meet the total demands of the environment

☒ **B** being healthy so that you are free from disease

☐ **C** complete health and wellbeing

☒ **D** complete emotional, social and physical wellbeing

(1 mark)

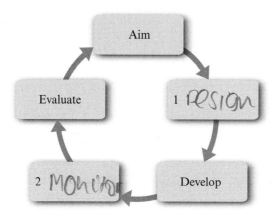

2 Complete the diagram by identifying the **two** missing stages in personal exercise programme development.

Aim

Evaluate

1 Design

2 Monitor

Develop

(2 marks)

3 Explain why it is important to be clear about your training aim before starting to plan a programme.

If you are unsure why you are training you will not be able to effectively
compete ....

....

.... **(2 marks)**

4 Explain how an understanding of training programme design can help improve health.

....

....

....

.... **(4 marks)**

> Think about all the phases of designing a programme from start to finish. How will these make sure your training is effective?

Physical health

1   **Figure 1** shows an individual participating in sport.

> Watch out for words like **different**. When you see them, make sure you give a broad range of answers. In this case, give examples from two different body systems.

   (a)   Identify **two** different physical health benefits the tennis player may gain through participation in physical activity.

....

....

....

....

Figure 1

(2 marks)

   (b)   Describe how the physical health benefits you identified in (a) can be achieved.

> Note that these questions are about physical **health**, not physical fitness.

....

....

....

....

....

....

....

....

(4 marks)

2   Complete the table below by stating the relevant long-term physical health benefits of regular training.

> Make sure that your answers state the potential benefit that is relevant to the example given.

Effect	Physical health benefit
Reduction in resting blood pressure	
Increased bone strength	
Weight loss when overweight	Less likely to become obese, therefore ....

(3 marks)

Had a go ☐   Nearly there ☐   Nailed it! ☐

Emotional health

1 Which **one** of the following is considered to be an emotional benefit of exercise?

☐ **A** working in a team

☐ **B** developing friendships

☐ **C** competition

☐ **D** improved co-ordination

(1 mark)

> Check your category and look out for similar words.

2 Membership of a sporting club is said to stimulate competition. State **two** ways that being a member of a football club would give players the opportunity to be competitive.

....

....

....

(2 marks)

3 Complete the statements below about the benefits gained from participating in physical activity.

> Guided

(a) Many people take part in physical activity to ......*relieve*...... stress. This is

an .... benefit of physical activity.

(2 marks)

(b) People who take part in physical activity, especially activities such as

gymnastics and dance, can gain an ....

appreciation of the activity, due to the quality of the movements being

performed.

(1 mark)

(c) People who participate in physical activity regularly are often disappointed

when they cannot train. One possible reason for this is that the body doesn't

release or manufacture as much .... as it

would normally release as a result of physical activity. The presence of this

chemical in the brain accounts for the ....

factor experienced by performers.

(2 marks)

4 An increase in self-esteem is an emotional benefit of taking part in physical activity. Briefly explain how taking part in physical activity can increase self-esteem.

....

....

....

(2 marks)

Social health

Guided

1   George is 16 years old. Although he has always enjoyed PE, he is very shy.

Complete the table below by explaining how, through joining a sports club, George may achieve two different types of social health benefit.

Benefit	How achieved
Making new friends	By joining a club, he will meet new people and can make friends with them

(4 marks)

2   The children in **Figure 1** are playing ten-pin bowling. Explain **two** ways that participation in a physical activity such as ten-pin bowling can improve social health.

> Even if you are not familiar with the activity, use the image to help.

....

....

....

....

....

....

....

....

....

Figure 1

(4 marks)

3   Desmond enjoys athletics and swimming and often runs or swims in his free time.

Explain how Desmond could use participation in these activities to improve his social health.

....

....

....

....

....

....

(3 marks)

Lifestyle choices 1

1   In the summer Albie and his friends go to the beach every day after school.
Figure 1 shows Albie and his friends playing volleyball at the beach.

Figure 1

Guided

(a) Using the information above and **Figure 1**, identify **two** positive lifestyle choices of this group.

They make time for rest from .... and ....

....   **(2 marks)**

(b) Explain why **one** of your answers to (a) is a positive lifestyle choice.

....

....

....

....

....   **(3 marks)**

EXAM ALERT

2   Explain how **one** poor lifestyle choice about eating can damage your health.

....

....

....

....

....

....

> There are four marks available for this question, so you need to develop the same point by expanding on it. It would be a good idea to use an example and think of the consequences and what that could lead to. You will only gain full marks for expanding one point and not for two separate ideas.

(4 marks)

Lifestyle choices 2

Guided

1 (a) Identify **two** body systems that are negatively impacted by smoking.

....

....

.... **(2 marks)**

(b) Smoking and drinking alcohol are considered to be socially acceptable or recreational forms of drug taking.

    (i) How does this differ from taking performance-enhancing drugs?

....

.... **(1 mark)**

    (ii) There are known health risks associated with smoking and drinking. Why are athletes still allowed to take these types of drugs?

....

.... **(1 mark)**

Guided

(c) Briefly explain **one** heath risk associated with smoking.

Smoking can cause .... This is because ....

....

....

.... **(2 marks)**

(d) Explain **one** heath risk associated with drinking alcohol.

....

....

....

.... **(3 marks)**

2 **Figure 1** shows Shaznay and her friends. Every week they spend time together on the beach.

Using **Figure 1**, identify the lifestyle choice that could have a negative impact on the physical health of some of this group.

> There is only one mark available for this question. You only need to identify so there is no need to provide any further development in your response.

Figure 1

.... **(1 mark)**

Had a go ☐   Nearly there ☐   Nailed it! ☐

Sedentary lifestyle

1 Define the term **sedentary lifestyle**.

....

.... **(1 mark)**

2 Complete the table by identifying the **three** health issues associated with a sedentary lifestyle.

> Guided

Examples of problems due to sedentary lifestyle	
(i)	Due to lack of weight-bearing activity
(ii)	Linked to low self-esteem and drop in brain function
(iii) Type 2 diabetes	Linked to overweight people

(2 marks)

3 Explain how a sedentary lifestyle could impact on a named component of fitness.

....

....

.... **(3 marks)**

4 A sedentary lifestyle can lead to children becoming overweight or obese.

> Guided

The graphs below show information about overweight and obese children in the UK. Analyse the data to determine patterns in obesity levels.

Use of data

☐ Overweight   ■ Obese

(Source: The Health and Social Care Information Centre)

Obesity levels for girls ....

The group with the highest obesity levels according to the data is ....

....

.... **(2 marks)**

Impact of a sedentary lifestyle on weight

1   Being **overweight**, **overfat** and **obese** are all conditions that can have a negative impact on the health of an individual.

(a)   Write each of these terms in one of the boxes below, placing the most dangerous condition in the first box, and the least dangerous to health in the third box.

Most dangerous ⟶ Least dangerous

(2 marks)

(b)   Explain why you have placed the terms in the order you chose.

Guided

If you are .... this can lead to a number of

health issues, such as ....

....

....

....

....

....

....   **(3 marks)**

2   Briefly explain how sustained involvement in physical activity could protect against obesity.

....

....

....

....   **(2 marks)**

> **Sustained** means that you keep doing something over a period of time, i.e. you train regularly as part of a lifestyle choice.

Diet and energy balance

1 In order to maintain a high level of performance, athletes need a good balance between exercise, diet, work and rest.

Figure 1 shows some suggested proportions for the different components that make up a balanced diet.

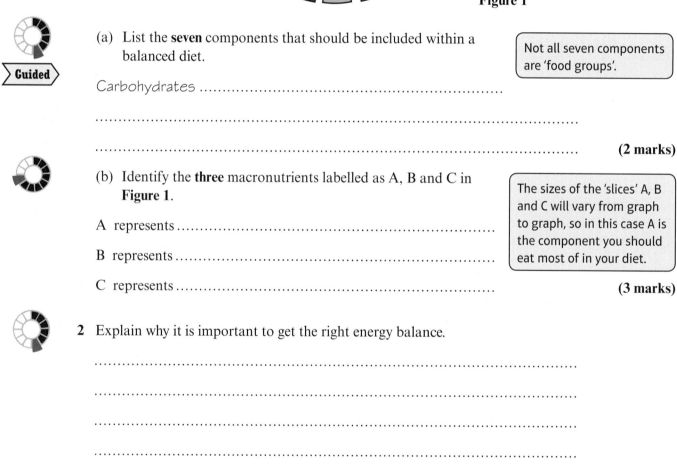

Figure 1

Guided

(a) List the **seven** components that should be included within a balanced diet.

> Not all seven components are 'food groups'.

Carbohydrates ....

....

.... **(2 marks)**

(b) Identify the **three** macronutrients labelled as A, B and C in **Figure 1**.

> The sizes of the 'slices' A, B and C will vary from graph to graph, so in this case A is the component you should eat most of in your diet.

A represents ....

B represents ....

C represents .... **(3 marks)**

2 Explain why it is important to get the right energy balance.

....

....

....

....

.... **(3 marks)**

Optimum weight

1 Define the term **optimum weight**.

....

....

.... **(2 marks)**

2 State how **four** different factors could cause a variation in an individual's optimum weight.

> Your height will affect your optimum weight.
>
> The taller you are, the more you will weigh

Use the number of marks available as a guide. There are 8 marks available and you have been asked to outline four factors. This means there will be a mark for each factor and each outline of that factor. Make sure you include four!

....

....

....

....

....

....

....

.... **(8 marks)**

3 Use examples to demonstrate why and how optimum weight can be different in one activity compared with another.

> A jockey's optimum weight will be different from a ....

....

....

....

....

.... **(4 marks)**

4 Using an example, explain why optimum weight can vary depending on the role of a performer within the same sport.

....

....

....

.... **(3 marks)**

Dietary manipulation

1 Define the term **dietary manipulation**.

....

.... **(1 mark)**

2 Which **one** of these performers is **least** likely to worry about their timing of protein intake?

☐ **A** sprinter

☐ **B** shot putter

☐ **C** long-distance cyclist

☐ **D** power lifter   **(1 mark)**

3 (a) Explain why some elite performers use carbohydrate loading.

Guided

EXAM ALERT

Carbohydrate loading is a strategy to ....

....

....

....

....

.... **(3 marks)**

> This question has two parts. Reference is made to **some** performers; therefore, you will need to think about those who will use it. The second part of the question asks why carbohydrate loading would be an advantage; that is, why would that particular group of athletes use carbohydrate loading.

(b) State approximately how many days before an event a performer would start carbohydrate loading.

.... **(1 mark)**

4 Explain why it is important to maintain hydration levels during physical activity.

....

....

....

....

....

.... **(3 marks)**

Classification of skills 1

1 Using the terms in the table, identify **three** continua used to classify skills in sport.

High organisation	Open	Basic (simple)
Complex	Low organisation	Closed

(3 marks)

2 Which **one** of the following is an open skill?

☐ **A** penalty flick in hockey

☐ **B** vault in gymnastics

☐ **C** receiving a serve in tennis

☐ **D** serve in badminton

(1 mark)

3 Define the term **closed skill**.

....

....

(1 mark)

Guided

EXAM ALERT

4 Give **one** example of a closed skill and briefly explain why it falls into this classification.

A vault in gymnastics is a closed skill. This is because

....

....

....

....

(3 marks)

> To **briefly explain** you need to demonstrate your knowledge and understanding of the topic by saying what makes a skill a closed skill.

Classification of skills 2

1   State **one** reason why recreational jogging is considered a basic skill.

....   **(1 mark)**

2   Which **one** of the following is the **most** complex skill?

☐   **A**   running on a track

☐   **B**   swimming in a pool

☐   **C**   laying up a shot in basketball

☐   **D**   cycling on a track   **(1 mark)**

3   State **two** characteristics of a complex skill.

....

....   **(2 marks)**

4   **Figure 1** shows performers passing the baton in a relay race. Explain where you would place this skill on the basic–complex continuum.

> Think about the type of skill. Is there much thought involved or information to process?

Figure 1

....

....

....

....   **(3 marks)**

5   Using an example, explain the classification of low organisation skills.

Guided

A tennis serve is an example of a low organisation skill because ....

....

....

....   **(3 marks)**

Massed and distributed practice

1 The netball coach at a junior school has started planning a practice session. Look at the start of the plan and identify the type of practice the coach is planning.

> Each performer takes 5 shots at a netball goal from 1 metre away
> 5 × chest passes to a partner 2 metres apart
> 5 × bounce passes to a partner 2 metres apart
> 2 minutes rest

.... **(1 mark)**

Guided

2 Explain why a coach may use distributed practice with their performers when they are learning to use the rings in gymnastics, as shown in **Figure 1**.

> Think about the type of skill. If you are not sure about this type of skill, use the picture as a guide to the things that would need to be considered.

The task is complex and could be ....

If they did massed practice ....

....

....

....

....

....

Figure 1

(3 marks)

3 (a) Describe one advantage **and** one disadvantage of massed practice.

....

....

.... **(2 marks)**

EXAM ALERT

(b) Describe one advantage **and** one disadvantage of distributed practice.

> Remember to make it clear which is the advantage and which is the disadvantage, so that it is obvious that *you* know which is which.

....

....

.... **(2 marks)**

Fixed and variable practice

1   Which **one** of the following statements relates to fixed practice?

☐   **A**   continuous practice with few or no breaks

☐   **B**   structured practice where breaks are given for recovery or feedback

☐   **C**   practice structured so the skill is developed in different situations

☐   **D**   practice structured so the skill is repeated in an unchanging situation   **(1 mark)**

2   Define the term **variable practice**.

....

....   **(1 mark)**

3   Using an example describe a fixed practice session.

....

....

....   **(3 marks)**

Guided

4   Using an example, explain when you would use variable practice to help develop a skill.

....

.... for example a return of service in tennis, so the

performer gets used to ....

....

....   **(3 marks)**

5   Explain the type of practice structure you would use with a group learning to dribble the ball in football.

....

....

Think about the nature of the skill of dribbling a ball. What type of practice is used with that type of skill?

....

....

....   **(3 marks)**

Values of goal setting 1

Guided

1 State three reasons why the use of goal setting is considered to be good practice.

It helps you to plan your training by giving specific focus. ....

....

....

....

....

....

.... **(3 marks)**

2 SMART targets should be specific. Give **one** example of a specific target for a squash player who plays in the third team at their local leisure centre.

....

.... **(1 mark)**

Guided

3 Give one example of a measurable target that the following performers may set themselves.

> Remember, for a target to be measurable you must be able to see if the target is met or not. It normally involves times or amounts.

(a) A sprinter who currently runs 100 m in 14.10 seconds.

Decrease time to 14.0 seconds **(1 mark)**

(b) A high jumper who has a personal best of 1 m 50 cm.

....

.... **(1 mark)**

(c) A games player who plays for the second team.

....

.... **(1 mark)**

(d) A striker in the first team who scores five goals in the first six weeks of the season.

....

.... **(1 mark)**

(e) A gymnast with a personal best tariff of 4.5.

....

.... **(1 mark)**

Values of goal setting 2

1 For each of the following statements, explain why the target is not achievable for the performer described in the statement.

(a) A sprinter who currently runs 100 m in 14.10 seconds is set a target of 12.00 seconds within the next two weeks.

....

....

....
(2 marks)

(b) A high jumper who has a personal best of fifth place when competing in county trials has been set a target of coming first at the next competition.

....

....

....
(2 marks)

(c) A striker in the first team who scored five goals in the first six weeks of the season is set a target of scoring 20 in the next six weeks.

....

....

....
(2 marks)

(d) A gymnast with a personal best tariff of 4.5 is set a target of achieving a 6.0 in their next competition.

....

....

....
(2 marks)

2 Give an example of a time-bound SMART target for a squash player who plays in the third team at their local leisure centre.

....

....
(1 mark)

3 Explain how **one** of the principles of SMART target setting could help maintain motivation to train.

> Choose one of the SMART principles and link it to motivation.

Guided

By setting a .... goal they can

monitor progress. Knowing their training is working will ....

....

....
(3 marks)

Visual and verbal guidance

1   Explain **one** of the qualities required to ensure visual guidance is successful.

....

....

....

.... **(3 marks)**

2   Explain why visual guidance is an appropriate type of guidance for a group of beginners learning to play an overhead clear in badminton, as in **Figure 1**.

> **Guided**

> Remember that **explain** means show your knowledge and understanding of the topic and then apply it.

Figure 1

....

.... By visually showing the performer the

technique they can form a ....

....

.... **(3 marks)**

3   (a)   State when a coach would use verbal guidance and give an example to support your answer.

....

.... **(2 marks)**

(b)   State one advantage **and** one disadvantage of verbal guidance.

> **EXAM ALERT**

....

....

> Remember to make it clear which is the advantage and which is the disadvantage, so that it is obvious that *you* know which is which.

....

.... **(2 marks)**

Had a go ☐ Nearly there ☐ Nailed it! ☐

Manual and mechanical guidance

1 Which **one** of the following statements relates to mechanical guidance?

☐ **A** using an aid to help a performer learn a skill

☐ **B** demonstrating how to complete a skill

☐ **C** physically supporting a performer to learn a skill

☐ **D** giving instruction on how to complete a skill

(1 mark)

2 State the difference between manual and mechanical guidance.

....

.... **(1 mark)**

3 State the type of guidance being used if a coach uses a tumbling belt to help a performer learn to somersault in trampolining.

.... **(1 mark)**

4 (a) Identify the type of guidance being used in **Figure 1**.

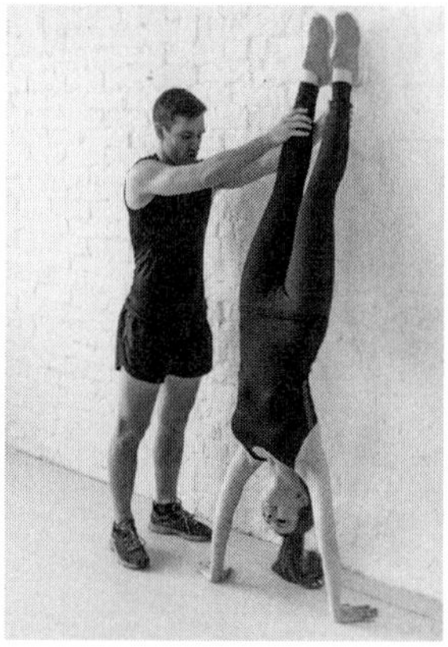

Figure 1

Use the image to help. What is the coach doing to help the performer?

.... **(1 mark)**

(b) Describe the type of guidance you identified in part (a).

....

....

.... **(2 marks)**

5 Explain why a swimming teacher with a group of 12 children is more likely to use mechanical guidance than manual guidance.

Guided

If the children are not strong swimmers they will need ....

....

....

.... **(3 marks)**

Types of feedback

1 Which **one** of the following is the **most appropriate** statement about concurrent feedback?

☐ **A** information about the quality of the skill from the performer's muscles

☐ **B** information given to the performer during performance

☐ **C** information given to the performer after they have completed the skill

☐ **D** information given to the performer by the coach or audience   **(1 mark)**

2 Briefly explain **one** reason why a coach would **not** need to use extrinsic feedback.

> **Guided**

Elite performers do not need extrinsic feedback because ....

....

.... **(2 marks)**

3 Using an example, describe when a coach would use terminal feedback.

....

.... **(2 marks)**

4 Explain **two** considerations for a coach deciding on the type of feedback to use.

....

....

....

.... **(4 marks)**

> This question asks you to **explain**, so make sure you provide a reason for each consideration you give within your answer.

5 **Figure 1** shows the number of successful basketball shots for two groups of beginners. Using the graph, analyse the effectiveness of the two types of feedback.

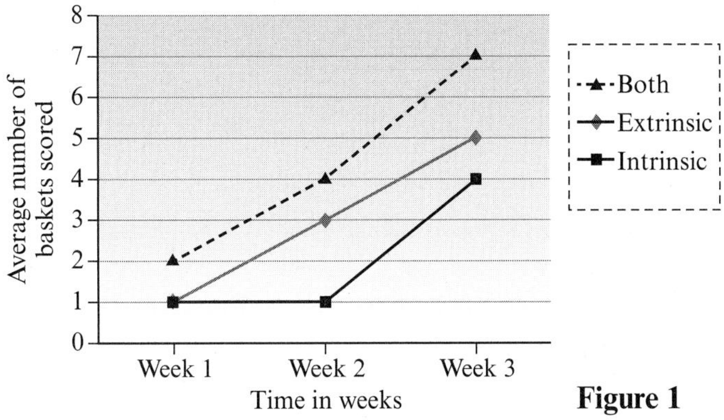

Use of data

Figure 1

....

....

....

.... **(4 marks)**

Mental rehearsal

1 Which **one** of the following is a correct statement about mental rehearsal?

☐ **A** It allows you to physically prepare for your activity.

☐ **B** It is a good substitute for physical practice.

☐ **C** It allows the performer to think about completing the action correctly.

☐ **D** It should only be completed by those who are injured.

(1 mark)

2 Define the term **mental rehearsal**.

....

....

(1 mark)

3 State when a performer would use mental rehearsal.

....

> If you rehearse something you practise it. When would you 'practise'?

....

(1 mark)

4 Describe when a games player such as a striker in football could use mental rehearsal.

....

....

....

....

(3 marks)

5 Using an example, explain **one** reason why mental rehearsal can be used more often in some sports than in others.

> Guided

Some activities are continuous, for example games, therefore the

players do not get a lot of time ....

....

....

....

....

....

(4 marks)

Socio-economic groups

1 (a) Using the data in **Table 1**, create a bar chart to represent the different percentage (%) levels of participation between 2012 and 2013 for:

- the highest socio-economic group
- the lowest socio-economic group.

One session a week (at least 4 sessions of at least moderate intensity for at least 30 minutes in the previous 28 days)	APS1 (Oct 2005–Oct 2006)		APS5 (Oct 2010–Oct 2011)		APS7 (Apr 2012–Apr 2013)		
	%	Number	%	Number	%	Number	Statistically significant change from APS1
NS SEC1–2 (managerial/professional)	40.1%	4,462,100	41.4%	4,812,000	41.3%	4,903,800	Increase
NS SEC3 (intermediate)	32.3%	1,244,000	32.4%	1,303,700	34.4%	1,415,900	Increase
NS SEC4 (small employers/own account workers)	32.4%	920,200	32.5%	958,400	32.7%	992,400	No change
NS SEC5–8 (long-term unemployed)	26.9%	3,450,200	26.6%	3,564,800	26.6%	3,639,900	No change

Table 1 (Source: Sport England's Active People Survey)   **(2 marks)**

(b) State **one** reason for the difference in participation rates between the socio-economic groups.

....

....

> A person's socio-economic group is based on the type of job they do. Why might this be relevant?

(2 marks)

2 Explain why your socio-economic group could affect the sports you participate in.

....

....

....

....

....

(4 marks)

3 Explain why the government collects data on participation rates in physical activity and sport.

....

....

....

(3 marks)

Gender and age groups

Use of data

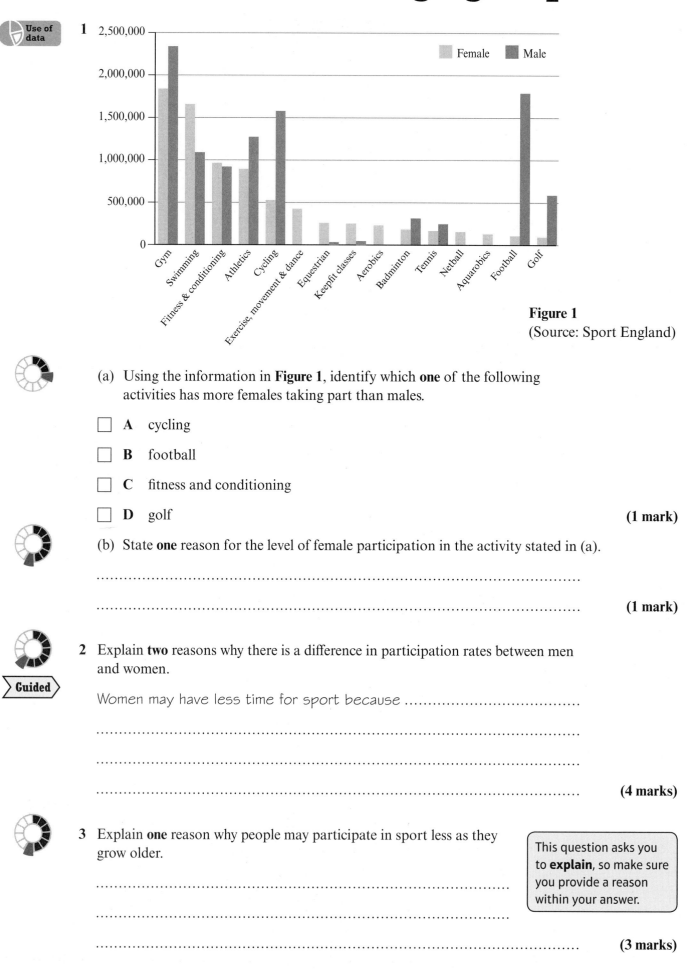

1

Figure 1
(Source: Sport England)

(a) Using the information in **Figure 1**, identify which **one** of the following activities has more females taking part than males.

☐ **A** cycling

☐ **B** football

☐ **C** fitness and conditioning

☐ **D** golf   **(1 mark)**

(b) State **one** reason for the level of female participation in the activity stated in (a).

....

.... **(1 mark)**

2 Explain **two** reasons why there is a difference in participation rates between men and women.

Guided

Women may have less time for sport because ....

....

....

.... **(4 marks)**

3 Explain **one** reason why people may participate in sport less as they grow older.

....

....

.... **(3 marks)**

> This question asks you to **explain**, so make sure you provide a reason within your answer.

Ethnicity and disability groups

1   **Figure 1** shows once a week disability participation rates in physical activity and sport from October 2006 to April 2015.

Use of data

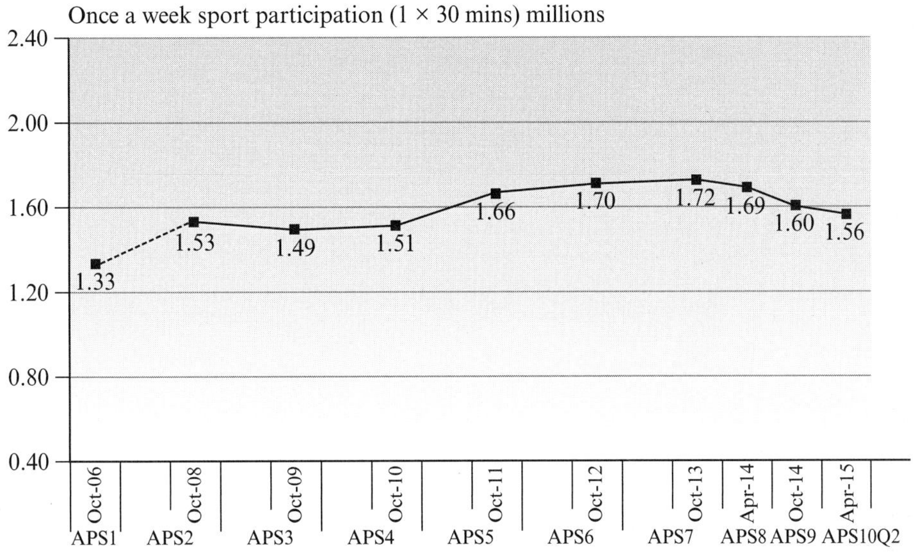

Once a week sport participation (1 × 30 mins) millions

Figure 1
(Source: Sport England)

Analyse the graph in **Figure 1** to determine the changing trends in participation rates between 2006 and 2015.

....

....

....

....

Remember, a **trend** is the general direction in which something is moving.

(4 marks)

2   Explain **two** reasons why participation rates in sport and physical activities are low among people with disabilities.

Guided

There could be a lack of .... For example,

a wheelchair user may want to play basketball, but may not live close

enough to a sports facility that offers this wheelchair activity. Or this

could be due to ....

....

....

(3 marks)

3   Using an example, explain how stereotyping can impact on participation rates of ethnic minority groups.

....

....

....

(3 marks)

Commercialisation, the media and sport

1 Define the term **commercialisation**.

....
(1 mark)

2 Identify the missing part of the golden triangle shown in **Figure 1**.

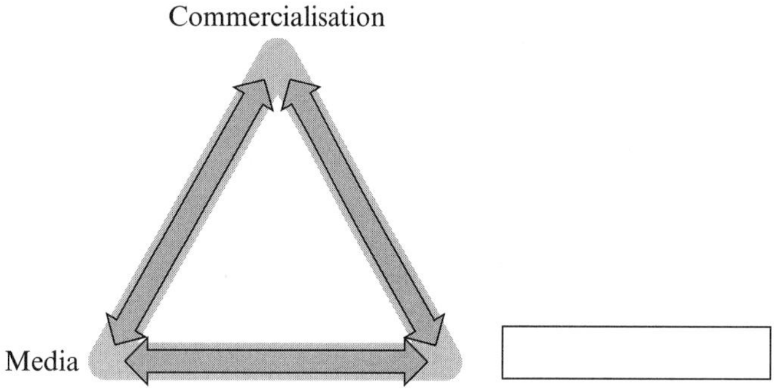

Commercialisation

Media

Figure 1 **(1 mark)**

3 State **two** ways that sport can attract funding.

....

....
(2 marks)

4 Using the data in **Table 1**, explain why companies such as Coca-Cola and McDonald's are prepared to pay millions of pounds to sponsor the Olympic Games.

Olympic Games	TV viewers worldwide
2014 (Sochi)	3.5 billion
2012 (London)	3.6 billion
2010 (Vancouver)	3.5 billion

Table 1 (Source: http://www. statista.com/statistics/287966/ olympic-games-tv-viewership-worldwide/)

....

....

....

....
(3 marks)

5 Explain the relationship between sport, commercialism and the media.

Guided

All three need each other to provide the money they

need to develop further. For example ....

....

....

....

....
(4 marks)

> A relationship is a connection between two or more things. You need to think about how each of these is connected to each of the others.

The advantages of commercialisation

1   Explain the relevance of the figures mentioned in **Figure 1** to the commercial organisations that were the official sponsors of the 2012 London Olympics.

> '... more than 51 million viewers aged 4+ watched television coverage of the Olympic Games, and over 31 million watched the Paralympic Games for 15 minutes or more, making the events the most-watched Games ever on UK television.'
> (Source: Ofcom)

Figure 1

....

....

....

.... **(3 marks)**

2   Explain why the men's 100 m sprint final at the 2012 London Olympics (**Figure 2**) was held on a Sunday evening.

....

....

....

....

....

Figure 2

.... **(3 marks)**

3   Explain **one** advantage of sponsorship to a performer.

Guided

....

which means that they can train full time and therefore ....

.... **(3 marks)**

4   Explain **one** advantage for spectators if their sport receives more funding.

> Make sure you read the question carefully. The focus of this question is the spectator and not the performer.

....

....

....

.... **(3 marks)**

109

The disadvantages of commercialisation

Guided

1   Using examples, describe **two** ways that sponsorship can be bad for sport.

Breaks in play for advertising purposes will ....

....

....

....

.... **(4 marks)**

2   Using an example, explain why a sports performer should not simply accept any sponsorship deal.

....

....

....

.... **(3 marks)**

3   Give **three** examples of the negative impact of commercialisation on the spectator.

....

....

....

.... **(3 marks)**

EXAM ALERT

4   Using an example, explain **one** way sponsoring an elite performer can be bad for the sponsorship company.

> Remember to read the question carefully, to ensure you are clear who is being disadvantaged.

....

....

....

.... **(3 marks)**

Sporting behaviour

1 Which **one** of the following is an example of gamesmanship?

    ☐ **A**   time wasting

    ☐ **B**   kicking the ball out of play when an opponent is injured

    ☐ **C**   showing respect to the officials

    ☐ **D**   shaking hands

> Try not to confuse the terms **gamesmanship** and **sportsmanship**. Remember that sportsmanship means being a 'sport' and is a good thing, whereas gamesmanship is not.

(1 mark)

2 **Figure 1** shows a player helping his opponent up.

Figure 1

Identify the type of sporting behaviour being shown.

.... **(1 mark)**

3 Using an example, describe gamesmanship.

....

....

....

.... **(3 marks)**

4 Using an example, explain how sportsmanship at elite level can help improve sporting behaviour at grassroots.

Guided

Elite sports men and women are role models to those who play the

sport at grassroots. This means ....

....

....

....

.... **(3 marks)**

Deviance in sport

1 There have been several instances in sports where a player has bitten one of their opponents, as shown in **Figure 1**.

(a) Give **one** reason why an elite performer might bite their opponent.

Figure 1

....

....

....   **(1 mark)**

(b) Explain why biting is deviant behaviour.

....

....

....

....   **(3 marks)**

2 State **two** reasons why an elite performer might be deviant in their sport.

....

....   **(2 marks)**

> Think about the rewards of winning. Why would a performer cheat?

3 100% Me is a campaign against taking performance-enhancing drugs. The campaign is about performers being successful and confident and retaining the values of clean, fair competition. 100% Me embodies and celebrates five key values: hard work, determination, passion, respect and integrity.

Explain why it is necessary to have campaigns such as 100% Me.

Campaigns such as 100% Me are necessary because not all sports

performers demonstrate these values. Therefore ....

....

....

....   **(4 marks)**

Component 2 – Extended answer question 1

Dimitri plays badminton. He is determined to improve his performance. He decides to set SMART targets as a first step to achieving his long-term goal.

Discuss Dimitri's use of target setting to improve his performance. Use examples to illustrate your answer.

> Remember to demonstrate **knowledge** of the topic, your ability to **apply** your knowledge to the topic and your ability to make a **judgement** based on the points you are making.

Short | Full

Short course candidates will need to answer extended answer questions, but will not need to know the content on this page. Look only at the skills here.

....

....

....

....

....

....

....

....

....

....

....

....

....

....

....

....

....

....

....

....

....

....

Had a go .... Nearly there .... Nailed it! ....

....

....   **(9 marks)**

Component 2 – Extended answer question 2

Evaluate the impact of personal factors on participation.

> Remember to demonstrate **knowledge** of the topic, your ability to **apply** your knowledge to the topic and your ability to make a **judgement** based on the points you are making.

....

....

....

....

....

....

....

....

....

....

....

....

....

....

....

....

....

....

....

....

....

....

....

....

....

(9 marks)

Multiple choice questions

For each question, choose an answer, A, B, C or D, and put a cross in the box ☒.

If you change your mind about an answer, put a line through the box ☒ and then mark your new answer with a cross ☒.

1   Which of the following is not a macronutrient?

☐ **A**   vitamins   ☐ **C**   fats

☐ **B**   carbohydrates   ☐ **D**   proteins   **(1 mark)**

2   Which of the following is not a long-term effect of physical activity on the respiratory system?

☐ **A**   increased number of alveoli   ☐ **C**   increased strength of the diaphragm

☐ **B**   increased strength of intercostal muscles   ☐ **D**   increased number of red blood cells   **(1 mark)**

3   Which of the following is not a benefit of a cool down?

☐ **A**   aids the removal of lactic acid

☐ **B**   prevents injury

☐ **C**   aids the removal of carbon dioxide

☐ **D**   helps bring the heart rate and breathing rate slowly back down   **(1 mark)**

4   Which of the following is an immediate effect of exercise on the cardiovascular system?

☐ **A**   increased heart rate   ☐ **C**   increased capillarisation

☐ **B**   increased breathing rate   ☐ **D**   increased oxygen debt   **(1 mark)**

5   Which of the following statements is correct regarding redistribution of blood flow during exercise?

☐ **A**   Vasoconstriction is the narrowing of blood vessels supplying the working muscles.

☐ **B**   Vasoconstriction is the widening of blood vessels supplying the working muscles.

☐ **C**   Vasodilation is the narrowing of blood vessels supplying the digestive system.

☐ **D**   Vasodilation is the widening of blood vessels supplying the working muscles.   **(1 mark)**

6   Read the statements and decide which is correct – A, B, C or D.

☐ **A**   Beta blockers speed up the heart.

☐ **B**   Beta blockers increase the number of red blood cells.

☐ **C**   Diuretics can be used to remove other drugs from the body.

☐ **D**   Diuretics slow down the heart beat.   **(1 mark)**

Had a go ☐   Nearly there ☐   Nailed it! ☐

Short answer questions

1 Describe how to calculate the correct target zone for an endurance athlete.

....

....

....   **(3 marks)**

2 State an appropriate fitness test to measure power **and** describe the test procedure.

Fitness test: ....   **(1 mark)**

Test procedure: ....   **(3 marks)**

....

....

3 Explain whether the shot put is an aerobic or an anaerobic activity.

Short Full

....

....   **(3 marks)**

4 When planning his PEP, Eddie applied the principle of progressive overload.

Describe the principle of progressive overload and state why it is necessary to include in your PEP.

....

....   **(2 marks)**

5 Describe how Eddie could apply progressive overload in his PEP, if he wants to improve his muscular endurance.

....

....   **(2 marks)**

6 SMART targets are set to make training more successful. Explain why targets should be measurable.

....

....   **(2 marks)**

Use of data questions

1 **Tables 1 and 2** show fitness data collected by two sportspeople: Katya and Dave.
Tables 3, 4 and 5 show the ratings for results in three of the tests.

Table 1

Katya's test results and heart rate (HR) information	
Sit and reach test	15 cm
35-metre sprint test	5.60 s
Grip dynamometer test	28
HR immediately after exercise	120
HR 1 minute after exercise	100
HR 2 minutes after exercise	80
HR 3 minutes after exercise	70

Table 2

Dave's test results and heart rate (HR) information	
Sit and reach test	15 cm
35-metre sprint test	5.60 s
Grip dynamometer test	39 kg
HR immediately after exercise	115
HR 1 minute after exercise	95
HR 2 minutes after exercise	80
HR 3 minutes after exercise	68

Table 3 Sit and reach test ratings – flexibility

Rating	Males (cm)	Females (cm)
Excellent	25+	20+
Very good	17	17
Good	15	16
Average	14	15
Poor	13	14
Very poor	9	10

Table 4 35-metre sprint test ratings – speed

Rating	Males (s)	Females (s)
Excellent	<4.80	<5.30
Good	4.80–5.09	5.30–5.59
Average	5.10–5.29	5.60–5.89
Fair	5.30–5.60	5.90–6.20
Poor	5.60+	6.20+

Table 5 Grip dynamometer test ratings – strength

Rating	Males aged 15–19y (kg)	Females aged 15–19y (kg)
Excellent	52+	32+
Good	47–51	28–31
Average	44–46	25–27
Fair	39–43	20–24
Poor	<39	<20

(a) Use Katya's and Dave's fitness test results to complete the table by identifying the performer with the **best** rating for:

   • speed   • flexibility.

   • strength   **(3 marks)**

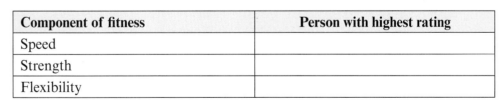

Component of fitness	Person with highest rating
Speed	
Strength	
Flexibility	

(b) Using the data in Table 1, complete the graph to show Katya's recovery heart rate.

(2 marks)

> If the data is about one category (for example, heart rate over time) you need to draw a line graph.

117

Extended answer questions 1

1   Despite being banned substances, there are a number of different performance-enhancing drugs available to sports performers should they choose to use them. Evaluate the benefits of EPO and diuretics on performance in endurance and power events.

> Remember to demonstrate **knowledge** of the topic, your ability to **apply** your knowledge to the topic and your ability to make a **judgement** based on the points you are making.

> It can be useful to write a brief plan so you cover all the main points in your essay. However do not use the answer space for your plan, as you should try to keep your answer to the space provided.

Short / **Full**

> Short course candidates will need to answer extended answer questions, but will not need to know the content on this page. Look only at the skills here.

....

....

....

....

....

....

....

....

....

....

....

....

....

....

....

....

....

....

....

....

....

....

....   **(9 marks)**

Extended answer questions 2

1 Mr Benson is training the school football team and has designed a weight training programme for the team to follow. Discuss whether weight training would be the most appropriate choice of training method for the football team.

> Remember to demonstrate **knowledge** of the topic, your ability to **apply** your knowledge to the topic and your ability to make a **judgement** based on the points you are making.

....

....

....

....

....

....

....

....

....

....

....

....

....

....

....

....

....

....

....

....

....

....

....

(9 marks)

Timed test 1

GCSE Physical Education

Paper 1 – Full course

Time: 1 hour 45 minutes

Instructions to candidates
- Use blue or black ink.
- Answer **ALL** questions.
- The total mark for this test is 90.

> **Theory Paper – Short Course**
>
> Time: 1 hour 30 minutes.
>
> Typical short course questions have been identified below.
>
> The short course exam will be marked out of 80 marks.

For each part of question 1, choose an answer, A, B, C or D, and put a cross in the box ☒.

Mark only one answer for each question. If you change your mind about an answer, put a line through the box ☒ and then mark your new answer with a cross ☒.

1 (a) Which **one** of the following movements occurs in the frontal plane about the sagittal axis?

　　☐ **A** back somersault

　　☐ **B** cartwheel

　　☐ **C** front somersault

　　☐ **D** full twist　　　　　　　　　　　　　　　　　　　　　**(1 mark)**

(b) Which one of the following is the correct definition of fitness?

　　☐ **A** a form of physical activity designed to bring about training adaptations

　　☐ **B** a lifestyle that contributes positively to physical, social and emotional health

　　☐ **C** the ability to use voluntary muscles many times without tiring

　　☐ **D** the ability to meet the demands of the environment　　　**(1 mark)**

(c) Which **one** of the following principles of training is likely to result in injury?

　　☐ **A** progressive overload

　　☐ **B** specificity

　　☐ **C** overtraining

　　☐ **D** individual needs　　　　　　　　　　　　　　　　　　**(1 mark)**

Short Full (d) Which of the following is a correct statement about the redistribution of blood flow during physical activity?

    ☐ **A** It increases the amount of blood flowing to the digestive system.

    ☐ **B** It increases the amount of blood allowed to circulate in the body.

    ☐ **C** It increases the amount of blood flowing to the working muscles.

    ☐ **D** It increases blood flow to the working muscles and digestive system. **(1 mark)**

Short Full (e) Which **one** of the following is an immediate effect of exercise on the cardiovascular system?

    ☐ **A** increased breathing rate

    ☐ **B** increased heart rate

    ☐ **C** increased tidal volume

    ☐ **D** increased capillarisation **(1 mark)**

Short Full (f) Which **one** of the following statements is correct in relation to oxygen debt?

    ☐ **A** It is the amount of carbon dioxide owed during exercise.

    ☐ **B** It occurs due to a build up of lactic acid.

    ☐ **C** It is caused by anaerobic respiration and is paid back after exercise.

    ☐ **D** It only occurs in aerobic events lasting more than 5 minutes. **(1 mark)**

(g) Which **one** of the following statements best describes the impact of the use of anabolic steroids?

    ☐ **A** It increases the oxygen-carrying capacity of the blood.

    ☐ **B** It increases the ability to train harder.

    ☐ **C** It increases the viscosity of the blood.

    ☐ **D** It decreases the chance of other drugs being detected. **(1 mark)**

Short Full (h) Which **one** of the following correctly identifies the movement possibilities at a hinge joint?

    ☐ **A** flexion, extension, adduction, abduction

    ☐ **B** abduction, adduction

    ☐ **C** abduction, adduction, rotation

    ☐ **D** flexion, extension **(1 mark)**

Short Full 2 One of the functions of the skeleton is to provide protection. Using an example, describe how the skeleton provides protection during physical activity.

....

....

.... **(2 marks)**

Short / Full 3 Label the location of the quadriceps and pectoralis major on **Figure 1** and then state their function below.

Figure 1

Quadriceps: ....

Pectoralis major: .... **(4 marks)**

Short / Full 4 **Figure 2** shows a gymnast on the rings. Analyse the muscle and joint action of the gymnast's lower body in **Figure 2** as they maintain this position.

Figure 2

....

....

....

.... **(4 marks)**

Short / Full 5 **Figure 3** shows a cross section of the heart. Label the structures of the heart identified as **A** and **B**. **(2 marks)**

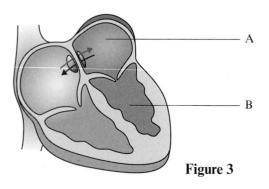

Figure 3

6 **Figure 4** shows a player injured during a game of rugby. Explain the role of blood in getting this player back on to the field of play.

Figure 4

....

....

.... **(3 marks)**

7 Briefly explain how the structure of the alveoli enables gas exchange at the lungs.

....

.... **(3 marks)**

8 Explain how the cardio-respiratory system ensures the muscles receive the oxygen they require for exercise.

....

....

.... **(3 marks)**

9 Explain one advantage **and** one disadvantage of anaerobic respiration.

....

....

.... **(3 marks)**

10 The table below lists some of the responses given by Year 10 students when asked what the effects of exercise are on the respiratory system.

Increased vital capacity	Increased lactic acid	Antagonistic action between lungs and alveoli
Hypertrophy of the lungs	Increased oxygen debt	Increased depth of breathing

Select the three correct responses and place each of the effects of exercise on the respiratory system into the correct box on the next page. **(3 marks)**

Immediate effect on the respiratory system	Effect of regular participation on the respiratory system

Short | Full

11 **Figure 5** shows the heart rate and breathing rate of a 20-year-old during different levels of exercise.

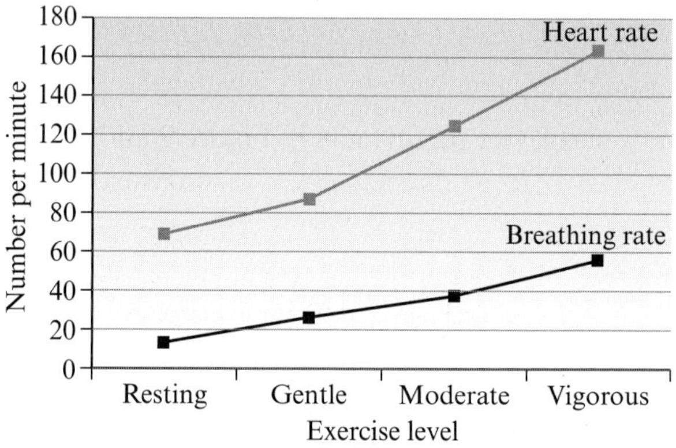

Figure 5

Analyse the data in **Figure 5** to determine the impact of exercise on an individual's heart and breathing rate.

....

....

....

.... **(4 marks)**

12 **Figure 6** shows a performer taking part in the vertical jump test.

Short | Full

(a) Identify the lever system acting at the ankle as the performer prepares to jump and then jumps.

....**(1 mark)**

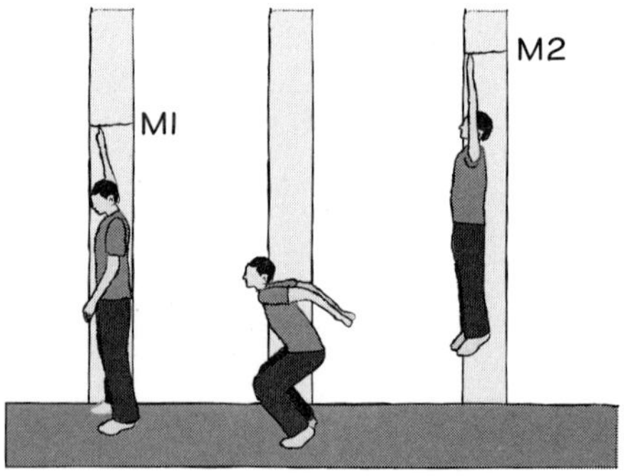

Figure 6

Short | Full

(b) Sketch this lever system. **(3 marks)**

13 **Figure 7** and **Figure 8** are sketches of two different classes of lever.

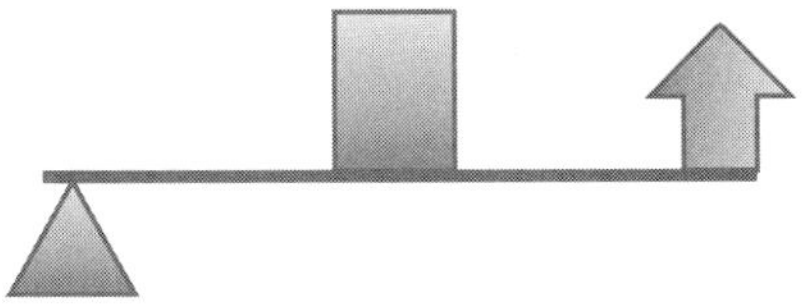

Figure 7 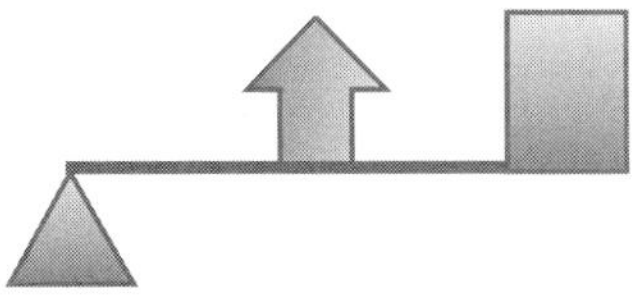   **Figure 8**

Short Full Explain which **one** of these lever systems will operate at a mechanical disadvantage.

....

....

.... **(3 marks)**

14 The performers in **Figure 9** and **Figure 10** require high levels of exercise and fitness to be the best in their activities.

Figure 9: 100 m sprinter    **Figure 10: Hurdler**

(a) Identify **one** component of fitness that both performers will utilise to achieve success in their event.

.... **(1 mark)**

(b) Explain how this component of fitness is used for both the sprinter **and** hurdler.

Sprinter: ....

....

Hurdler: ....

.... **(2 marks)**

(c) Identify an aspect of fitness that is more relevant to the hurdler and explain your choice.

Aspect of fitness: ....

Explanation: ....

.... **(3 marks)**

15 Describe the difference between muscular endurance and cardiovascular fitness.

....

.... **(3 marks)**

16 Coaches will measure the fitness of their performers using a range of fitness tests.

In the table below:

- identify the component of fitness being measured
- state an activity where performers of this activity would find the test useful.

Use a different activity for each test. **(6 marks)**

Fitness test	Component of fitness being measured	Activity where performers would find the test useful
Harvard step test		
Vertical jump test		
One-minute sit-up test		

17 Explain how a basketball coach could use fitness testing to improve the performance of her basketball players.

....

....

.... **(3 marks)**

18 Identify **three** different risks and the preventative measures that may be taken, that are associated with team games such as hockey and rugby.

....

....

.... **(3 marks)**

19 At the start of each session, a coach always uses a warm up. State **three** reasons why you should warm up before physical activity.

....

....

.... **(3 marks)**

20 Explain why blood doping is banned even though it is not a performance-enhancing drug.

....

.... **(3 marks)**

Short Full

21 Evaluate the long-term training effects of regular participation in physical activity on the cardiovascular system, and why those effects are important to performance in endurance events.

....

....

....

....

....

....

....

....

....

....

....

....

....

.... **(9 marks)**

22 **Figure 11** shows a tennis player during a match. Assess the importance of muscular endurance, flexibility and speed on performance in a tennis match.

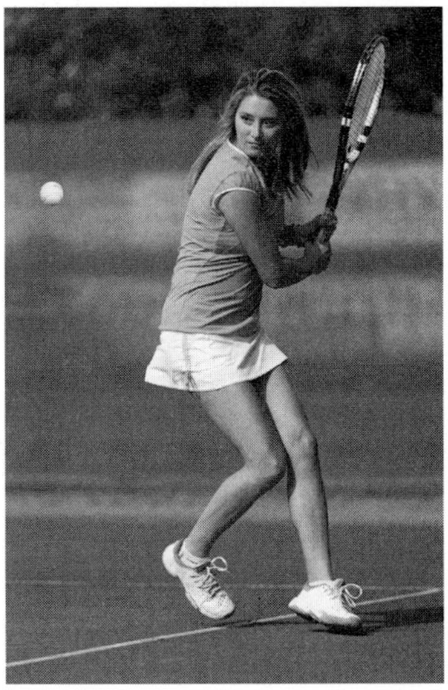

Figure 11

....

....

....

....

....

....

....

....

....

....

....

....

....

.... **(9 marks)**

Timed test 2

GCSE Physical Education

Paper 2

Time: 1 hour 15 minutes

Instructions to candidates

• Use blue or black ink.

• Answer **ALL** questions.

• The total mark for this test is 70.

Theory Paper – Short Course

Time: 1 hour 30 minutes.

Typical short course questions have been identified below.

The short course exam will be marked out of 80 marks.

Questions on this timed test related to health, well-being and lifestyle are relevant but the questions on sports psychology and social issues are not on the short course specification.

For each part of question 1, choose an answer, A, B, C or D, and put a cross in the box ☒.

Mark only one answer for each question. If you change your mind about an answer, put a line through the box ☒ and then mark your new answer with a cross ☒.

Short　Full   **1**   (a)   Which **one** of the following is a correct statement about self-esteem?

     ☐   **A**   It means self-centred, a player who does not pass in a game.

     ☐   **B**   It is a social benefit of exercise.

     ☐   **C**   It can be achieved by becoming better at sport.

     ☐   **D**   It happens after a losing streak when you play team games.   **(1 mark)**

Short　Full   (b)   Which **one** of the following gives the correct order for the development of a personal exercise programme?

     ☐   **A**   aim, evaluate, monitor, develop

     ☐   **B**   design, develop, monitor, evaluate

     ☐   **C**   monitor, design, aim, evaluate

     ☐   **D**   evaluate, design, aim, monitor   **(1 mark)**

Short　Full   (c)   Which **one** of the following could be due to additional muscle rather than fat?

     ☐   **A**   overweight

     ☐   **B**   overfat

     ☐   **C**   obese

     ☐   **D**   anorexic   **(1 mark)**

(d) Which **one** of the following skills would you classify as high organisation?

- [ ] **A** tennis serve
- [ ] **B** triple jump
- [ ] **C** golf swing
- [ ] **D** sprint start

(1 mark)

(e) Which **one** of the following targets is specific and measureable?

- [ ] **A** get better at long jump in the next three weeks
- [ ] **B** improve my basketball set shot
- [ ] **C** run the 100 m in a faster time
- [ ] **D** complete the 800 m 1 second faster

(1 mark)

(f) Which one of the following is an example of gamesmanship?

- [ ] **A** fouling a player and getting a red card
- [ ] **B** clapping the opponent when they make an error
- [ ] **C** kicking the ball off the field of play if an opponent is injured
- [ ] **D** shaking hands with opponent after the event

(1 mark)

`Short` `Full` **2** Explain **one** physical health benefit that can be gained through improving fitness.

....

.... **(4 marks)**

`Short` `Full` **3** Complete the statements about the benefits of regular exercise to health.

(a) Stress relief is an .... health benefit and reduces

stress-related illnesses such as .... **(2 marks)**

(b) Working in a team helps to improve .... This is a

.... health benefit. **(2 marks)**

`Short` `Full` **4** Describe **one** possible impact of serotonin on an individual and their willingness to participate in physical activity.

....

.... **(3 marks)**

`Short` `Full` **5** Bad choices regarding the food you eat can lead to obesity. Explain **one** other way that poor lifestyle choices about eating can damage your health.

....

....

.... **(4 marks)**

Short Full **6** (a) Explain the effect of smoking on the alveoli–gaseous exchange and the possible impact of this on fitness levels.

....

....

.... **(2 marks)**

Short Full (b) Identify **two** health risks to the respiratory system associated with smoking.

....

.... **(2 marks)**

Short Full **7** (a) Analyse the graph shown in **Figure 1** to determine the link between inactivity and increased risk of disease.

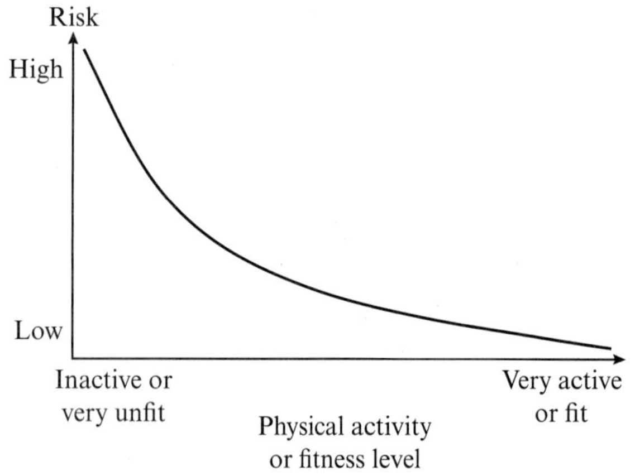

Figure 1

....

.... **(2 marks)**

Short Full (b) Identify **one** disease or health condition associated with a sedentary lifestyle.

.... **(1 mark)**

Short Full **8** (a) The table below lists the required components of a balanced diet.

Fats	Vitamins	Carbohydrates	Fibre
Water	Protein	Minerals	

Place the relevant components into the correct box below.

Note that not all components will be placed. **(3 marks)**

Macronutrients

Micronutrients

Short | Full

(b) Explain the link between diet, exercise and health.

....

....

.... **(4 marks)**

9 (a) State why it is an advantage for sports coaches to know the classification of a skill.

.... **(1 mark)**

(b) State the skill continuum being described:

> Skills on this continuum need to be either constantly adapted when being performed or performed in the same way every time.

.... **(1 mark)**

(c) State an example of a skill on the continuum you identified in (b) and justify your classification.

.... **(3 marks)**

10 Explain **one** way the personal factors of age **and** gender can impact on participation in physical activity.

....

....

.... **(4 marks)**

11 **Figure 2** shows the value of four sponsorship deals made between sports companies and sports performers.

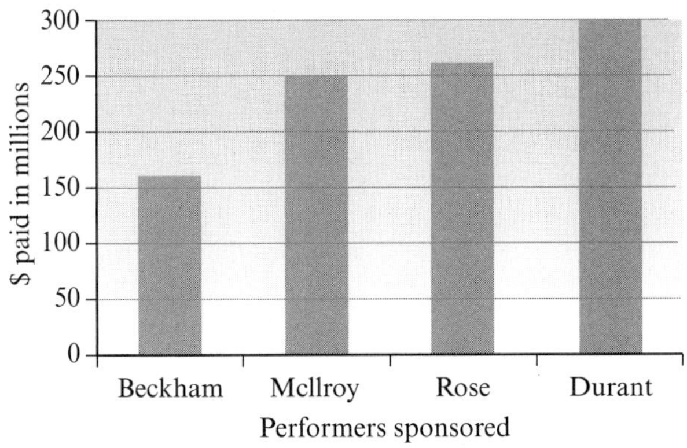

Figure 2 (Source: http://www.therichest.com/rich-list/the-biggest/10-of-the-biggest-sponsorship-deals-in-the-world/)

Explain why a sports clothing and equipment company would sponsor elite performers to such an extent.

....

....

.... **(4 marks)**

12 Table 1 shows Summer Olympic Games doping cases from 1968 to 2012.

Year	Place	Drug tests	Doping cases reported	
2012	London, England	5,051	9	0.18%
2008	Beijing, China	4,770	20	0.42%
2004	Athens, Greece	3,667	26	0.74%
2000	Sydney, Australia	2,359	11	0.47%
1996	Atlanta, USA	1,923	2	0.10%
1992	Barcelona, Spain	1,848	5	0.27%
1988	Seoul, S. Korea	1,598	10	0.63%
1984	Los Angeles, USA	1,507	12	0.80%
1980	Moscow, Russia	645	0	0.00%
1976	Montreal, Canada	786	11	1.40%
1972	Munich, Germany	2,079	7	0.34%
1968	Mexico City, Mexico	667	1	0.15%
	Total	**26,900**	**114**	**0.42%**

Table 1 (Source: ProCon.org)

Analyse **Table 1** to determine the trends in taking performance-enhancing drugs at the Olympics.

....

....

....

....

....

....

....

....

....

....   **(4 marks)**

Short / Full

13 Figure 3 shows a group of friends.

Evaluate the lifestyle choices shown in **Figure 3** and the impact these could have on the health of the individuals.

Figure 3

....

....

....

....

....

....

....

....

....

....

(9 marks)

14 Figures 4, **5** and **6** show some of the skills of basketball.

Figure 4

Figure 5

Figure 6

Analyse **Figures 4**, **5** and **6** to determine the most appropriate practice structures a coach should use to develop the skills associated with this activity.

....

....

....

....

....

....

....

....

....

....

(9 marks)

Answers

The following pages contain examples of answers that could be made to the questions throughout the workbook and timed tests. In many cases these are not the only correct answers.

1. Functions of the skeleton

1 (a) Students suggest two examples; sample answers are given below.
   (i) The skull protects the brain (1) if hit in the head by a hockey stick (1).
   (ii) The ribcage protects the heart and lungs (1) if hit in the chest by a golf ball (1).
   (b) Function: blood cell production (1); movement (1). Example: Platelets clot blood if cut playing rugby (1); works with muscles to move limbs – for example, the arm when playing tennis (1)
2 **Figure 1**: The skeleton supports the boxer (1) by keeping him in an upright position (1).
   Figure 2: The ribcage protects the heart and lungs (1) if hit in the chest by a cricket ball (1).
3 Bones (1); levers (1); movement (1); muscles (1)

2. Classification of bones

1 Irregular (1)
2 **C** The cranium is a flat bone. (1)
3 The sternum is a flat bone. (1) It is used for protection: for example to protect the chest if hit by a cricket ball. (1) The pelvis is another example of a flat bone. (1) It provides a place for muscle attachment, for example, the hip flexors attach to the pelvis to assist with running. (1)
4 (a) **B** (1)
   (b) Short bones (1)

3. Structure of the skeleton

1 (a) Radius (1); ulna (1)
   (b) Phalanges (1)
2 **B** = thoracic (1); **D** = sacrum (1)
3 **A** = ribs (1); **B** = sternum (1); protect the heart (1): for example, from a punch to the chest in boxing (1)
4 The femur is located in the upper leg. (1) It forms a joint with the patella/tibia/pelvis. (1)

4. Classification of joints

1 (a) The place where two or more bones meet
   (b) **Joint A**: name – elbow (1), type – hinge (1);
       Joint B: name – hip (1), type – ball and socket (1)
2 **C** = wrist (1)
3 The elbow is a hinge joint. The range of movement at a hinge joint is flexion and extension (1): for example, a biceps curl during weightlifting (1).

5. Movement at joints 1

1 (a) Reduction of the angle at a joint (1); example: the arm at the elbow in preparation for a chest pass (1)
   (b) Increase of the angle at a joint (1); example: the arm held straight when blocking in volleyball (1)
2 (a) **Figure 1**: Knees (1); hip (1)
       Figure 2: Elbows (player with ball) (1); hips (1); knees (1)
   (b) **Figure 3**: Elbows (1); right hip (1); right knee (1)
       Figure 4: left elbow (player without ball) (1); wrists (1)

6. Movement at joints 2

1 (a) Abduction is movement of a limb away from the body (1): for example, a cartwheel (1).
   (b) Rotation is circular movement at a joint. (1): for example, the overarm bowling action in cricket (1)
2 (a) **Figure 1** (1)
   (b) **C** = Both images show abduction of the arm at the shoulder. (1)

7. Movement at joints 3

1 Circumduction (1)
2 (a) Bending the foot at the ankle so the toes come up towards the leg (1) – this happens in the leg shoot in the long jump (1)
   (b) Moving the foot downwards at the ankle, pointing the toes (1) – this happens in a pike position in diving when the performer is trying to make the dive look good (1)
3 Plantar-flexion is occurring at the ankle of the leg about to kick the ball. (1) This means that the toes are pointed downwards in preparation to kick the ball. (1) The action at the ankle next to the ball is dorsi-flexion. (1) The foot is firmly placed on the ground to help keep balance. (1)

8. Ligaments, tendons and muscle types

1 Tendon (1)
2 Ligaments join bone to bone (1) to help stabilise joints (1).
3 Involuntary (1)
4 The blood vessels contain involuntary muscle (1); this means they contract automatically (1).
5 Cardiac (1)
6 Tendons attach muscle to bone. (1) This means that when the muscle contracts it can pull the bone as it is attached to it via the tendon, and therefore it allows movement. (1)

9. Muscles

1 (a) Pectoralis major – upper chest (1); external obliques – side of abdomen (1)
   (b) The player will need to turn their upper body to play a backhand; they are able to rotate due to the action of the external obliques. (1) Pectoralis major will be used to move the racket across the body when playing a forehand. (1)
2 Lines between external obliques and rotates the trunk (1) and between deltoid and abducts the arm at the shoulder (1).
3 Muscle **A** is the latissimus dorsi. (1) The role of muscle **A** is it adducts the upper arm at the shoulder. (1)

10. Antagonistic muscle pairs: biceps and triceps

1 Biceps (1)
2 (a) Skeletal muscles work together to provide movement: while one muscle contracts another relaxes (1), causing the bone they are attached to move (1).
   (b) Triceps (1)
   (c) When the biceps contract the triceps relaxes. (1) This allows the runner to bend the arm at the elbow. To take the arm back again the biceps relax and the triceps contract. (1)
   (d) It allows the sprinter to 'pump' the arms (1), adding more power allowing him to run faster (1).
   (e) There is flexion and extension of the arm at the elbow (1).

11. Antagonistic muscle pairs: quadriceps and hamstrings

1 (a) (i) Quadriceps (1); (ii) extends the leg at the knee (1)
   (b) One example is the follow through with the leg after taking a shot at goal in football. (1) Another example is performing a pike jump in trampolining. (1) A third example is during the drive phase when running the 100 m sprint. (1)
   (c) (i) Hamstrings (1); (ii) to flex the leg at the knee (1); (iii) possible example: In gymnastics when tucking the knees up to increase speed of rotation in a tumbling move (1).

12. Antagonistic muscle pairs: gastrocnemius and tibialis anterior

1 The muscles in the lower leg are the gastrocnemius and tibialis anterior. **(1)** By contracting the gastrocnemius and relaxing the tibialis anterior **(1)** the netballers are able to jump to reach the ball. **(1)**

2 (a) Gastrocnemius **(1)**

   (b) One example is pointing the toes when diving. **(1)** Other examples are kicking a ball with the laces **(1)** and going up on toes in ballet. **(1)**

3 The gastrocnemius and tibialis anterior are working as an antagonistic pair. **(1)** The tibialis anterior contracts **(1)** to dorsi-flex the foot **(1)** while the gastrocnemius relaxes enabling the long jumper to bring the toe up in the position shown **(1)**.

13. Antagonistic muscle pairs: hip flexors and gluteus maximus

1 **A** = hip flexors (1); **B** = gluteus maximus **(1)**

2 (a) Taking the leg back at the hip **(1)** so the angle of the joint increases **(1)**

   (b) Gluteus maximus **(1)**

   (c) During take off in the high jump: the hip extends to get the shape required to clear the bar **(1)**

3 (a) Hip flexion **(1)**

   (b) Hip flexors **(1)**

4 The gluteus maximus is the agonist, taking the leg back to extend the hip in the preparation phase **(1)**; the hip flexors are the antagonist in this movement **(1)**. Then to bring the leg through to strike the ball and flexing the hip, the hip flexors are the agonists **(1)** and the gluteus maximus becomes the antagonist **(1)**.

14. Muscle fibre types

1 **Figure 1**: Fast twitch type IIx **(1)**; **Figure 2**: slow twitch type I **(1)**

2 **B** medium speed of contraction **(1)**

3 (a) Fast twitch type IIx **(1)**; (b) medium to high **(1)**; (c) high **(1)**

4 Fast twitch type IIx muscles can contract the most forcibly of the fibre types. **(1)** Therefore they can produce more power. **(1)** So with more of these fibres the 100 m sprinter would be able to generate more power to increase her speed during the race. **(1)**

15. Cardiovascular system 1

1 Heart **(1)**; blood vessels **(1)**; blood **(1)**

2 (a) (i) Transport of oxygen **(1)**; (ii) clotting of open wounds **(1)**; (iii) transport of carbon dioxide **(1)**

   (b) For example: Oxygen is transported in the blood to the muscles. **(1)** The muscles are able to use this oxygen in energy production **(1)** so that the performer has the energy required to do the physical work they need to do in their activity **(1)**.

3 The blood vessels vasoconstrict. **(1)**

4 Carbon dioxide **(1)**

5 The blood vessels under the skin increase in diameter. **(1)** This is called vasodilation. **(1)** This increases blood flow to the capillaries under the surface of the skin **(1)** so heat can radiate from the skin, helping to reduce body temperature **(1)**.

16. Cardiovascular system 2

1 (a) **A** Right atrium **(1)**; **B** aorta **(1)**

   (b) The aorta is the main artery **(1)** that carries oxygenated blood to the muscles **(1)**.

2 The bicuspid valve is located between the left atrium and left ventricle. **(1)** It prevents backflow of blood **(1)** so that oxygenated blood can move through the heart and then out to the working muscles for energy production **(1)**.

3 **B** The septum separates the left and right sides of the heart. **(1)**

4 The vena cava is the main vein **(1)** that transports blood to the heart **(1)**. The blood is deoxygenated **(1)** as the working muscles have used the oxygen during physical activity **(1)**.

17. Blood vessels

1 (i) Arteries **(1)**; (ii) capillaries **(1)**; (iii) veins **(1)**

2 Artery **(1)**

3 The role of veins is to return blood to the heart after it has circulated the body **(1)**. This means the blood will be at low pressure **(1)**, therefore the veins need valves to prevent backflow of blood away from the heart **(1)**.

4 The role of the capillaries is to allow gaseous exchange **(1)** by taking oxygen from the alveoli into the bloodstream **(1)** and then from the bloodstream to the muscles **(1)**. The capillaries can make sure oxygen is delivered to the muscles for energy production for aerobic activity. **(1)**

5 Arteries are designed to help regulate blood pressure. **(1)** They have thick muscular walls **(1)**, which allows them to squeeze and contract to regulate blood flow **(1)**. When they relax this increases the internal diameter of the blood vessel, reducing blood pressure, as there is more room for the blood **(1)**.

18. Vascular shunting

1 Vascular shunting is the term for the process when blood flow to different parts of the body is altered depending on demand for oxygen. **(1)** For example, when exercising blood flow is increased to active areas **(1)** and decreased to inactive areas such as the digestive system **(1)**.

2 (a) Vasodilation is the widening of the lumen of the blood vessels **(1)** and vasoconstriction is the narrowing of the lumen of the blood vessels **(1)**. By altering the internal diameter of the blood vessel the body can regulate the amount of blood flowing to different areas of the body during exercise. **(1)** Therefore, the blood vessels supplying the digestive system vasoconstrict to reduce blood flow to this area of the body. **(1)**

   (b) Vascular shunting as a result of exercise will increase blood flow to the working muscles. **(1)** This means greater energy production for the performer. **(1)** However, if the performer has just eaten there will be conflicting demands for additional blood flow **(1)**: the digestive system will need more blood for digestion but will not receive enough due to the demands of the muscles, leading to undigested food. **(1)**

3 At rest blood flow is focused on the digestive system, with 45% going to this area of the body. **(1)** At rest the muscles only receive 20% of the blood flow. **(1)** However, during exercise blood flow increases dramatically to the muscles, from 20% to 80%, as these have now become active **(1)**, and blood flow to the digestive system is greatly reduced, dropping from 45% of blood flow to 5% **(1)**.

19. Plasma, platelets and blood cells

1 Red blood cells **(1)**; white blood cells **(1)**; platelets **(1)**

2 Binna can return to the game as the platelets **(1)** formed a clot at the site of the wound, **(1)** preventing further blood loss and preventing her from being a potential risk to others. **(1)**

3 During a long-distance race, runners will need a constant supply of oxygen for energy production. **(1)** This oxygen is carried by the red blood cells in the plasma. **(1)** Without this continuous supply of oxygen the runner would not be able to produce energy aerobically **(1)** and would therefore need to slow down or stop to recover, increasing their race time **(1)**.

4 Elite performers can only train effectively if they are healthy. **(1)** If they catch a cold or become unwell, their white blood cells will attack the infection, reducing the amount of time they are unwell and have to stop training. **(1)** This would allow them to maintain fitness so the quality of their performance would be unaffected. **(1)**

20. Composition of air

1 Inhaled air is air breathed in, exhaled air is air breathed out. **(1)**

2 (i) inhaled = **A**; (ii) exhaled = **C**

3 Exhaled air has a higher percentage of carbon dioxide than inhaled air **(1)**, because the body produces carbon dioxide **(1)** during aerobic exercise **(1)**.

4 The impact of physical activity on oxygen levels in exhaled air is that the oxygen levels drop **(1)**. This is because during exercise oxygen is used. **(1)** This oxygen is taken from the amount of oxygen breathed in, and therefore there is less to breathe out. **(1)**

21. Lung volumes

1 **C** Tidal volume **(1)**
2 Tidal volume is the amount of air moving into and out of the lungs during normal breathing. Therefore as the performer works harder – for example, when sprinting for the ball – their tidal volume will increase **(1)** to take greater amounts of air containing oxygen into the lungs **(1)** to be delivered to the muscles for energy production **(1)**. Even though the player reduces their pace, their tidal volume will remain elevated to aid recovery from the higher level of activity, though not as high as there is a reduced demand for oxygen since they are not working as hard. **(1)**
3 (a) At rest the tidal volume is 0.5 litres. **(1)** The vital capacity is 2.5 litres. **(1)**.
  (b) Vital capacity would remain the same **(1)** as this is the maximum forced expiration or inspiration so cannot alter as it is already at maximum **(1)**. However, the depth of the traces for tidal volume will increase **(1)**, as depth of breathing increases to allow more oxygen to enter the body via inhaled air, providing increased oxygen for energy production for exercise **(1)**.

22. The respiratory system

1 (a) **Diaphragm** During inspiration the diaphragm contracts and flattens **(1)** to make more space in the chest so the lungs can expand to pull in air **(1)**.
  Bronchioles The bronchioles form the link between the larger bronchi and the alveoli **(1)** so that air containing oxygen can travel into the lungs **(1)**.
  (b) Diagram labelled as follows:

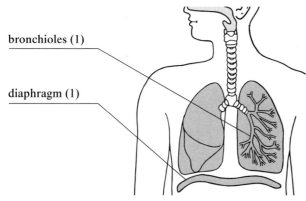

  bronchioles **(1)**

  diaphragm **(1)**

  (c) Inspiration **(1)**, as the diaphragm is flat **(1),** which occurs during inspiration to increase the space in the lungs to take in more air **(1)**

23. The alveoli and gas exchange

1 **D** thin-walled **(1)**
2 Arrows should show oxygen entering the tissues **(1)** and carbon dioxide leaving the tissues to join the blood **(1)**.
3 Capillaries around the muscle tissue contain blood with high levels of oxygen and low levels of carbon dioxide. **(1)** At the muscle tissue there are low levels of oxygen and high levels of carbon dioxide. **(1)** The gases will move from a high concentration to a low concentration **(1)** causing movement of oxygen from the blood into the muscle tissue and carbon dioxide from the muscle tissue into the blood **(1)**.
4 Capillaries around the alveoli contain blood with a low concentration of oxygen and a high concentration of carbon dioxide. **(1)**. Within the alveoli is a high concentration of oxygen and a low concentration of carbon dioxide. **(1)** Because gases will always try to have an equal concentration **(1)** the gases will move between the capillary and the alveoli, resulting in movement of oxygen from the alveoli into the blood and carbon dioxide from the blood into the alveoli **(1)**.

24. Energy and energy sources

1 Carbohydrates **(1)**
2 **C** a tennis player serving an ace **(1)**
3 **D** lactic acid **(1)**
4 Example: Squash **(i)** Maintaining the ability to continue to play long rallies throughout the game will require aerobic respiration. **(1)**; **(ii)** If the player has to quickly sprint to the front wall to retrieve a drop shot, this increased intensity will require anaerobic respiration. **(1)**
5 To respire aerobically the body needs glucose and oxygen **(1)**, whereas anaerobic respiration does not require oxygen **(1)**. The two processes of respiration produce different by-products: carbon dioxide is produced aerobically **(1)**; lactic acid is produced anaerobically **(1)**.

25. Short-term effects of exercise on the muscular system

1 Temporary changes to the body in response to exercise **(1)**
2 Muscle fatigue/lactate accumulation **(1)**
3 **D** increase in lactate **(1)**
4 They may experience increased demand for energy for muscle contraction **(1)** due to the additional work being carried out by the muscles when running compared to when at rest **(1)**. Depending on the time taken to complete the race, they may also experience lactate accumulation **(1)**, as there is insufficient oxygen to break it down during energy production **(1)**.
5 They may experience muscle fatigue. **(1)** This occurs when the muscle is not able to produce the energy it needs for the level of activity due to an increase in acidity in the muscle cells. **(1)** This slows energy production **(1)**, meaning that the muscles have to reduce the intensity they are working at to allow the muscles time to recover **(1)**.

26. Short-term effects of exercise on the cardio-respiratory system

1 **D** increase in blood pressure **(1)**
2 Vascular shunting occurs **(1)** where blood is redirected away from inactive areas **(1)** to active areas such as the muscles **(1)**.
3 When we exercise the muscles need more energy to carry out the additional physical work required. **(1)** Therefore they will need a greater supply of oxygen and nutrients. **(1)** As these are transported in the blood the heart needs to beat quicker so their delivery to the muscles is quicker. **(1)**
4 **Figure 1** shows that the breathing rate immediately after exercise is higher than the resting breathing rate. **(1)** This is because even though the body has stopped exercising it needs more oxygen than normally required at rest **(1)** to help the body recover from the exercise **(1)**. The additional oxygen is used to break down any lactate that accumulated during exercise. **(1)**

27. Lever systems 1

1 **B** ■ ▲ ⇨ ———— **(1)**

2

Parts of the body	Component of a lever system
Elbow joint	Fulcrum **(1)**
Radius	Lever **(1)**
Weight of the hand	Load **(1)**
Biceps	Effort **(1)**

3 Fulcrum **(1)**
4 A first class lever system can be found at the atlas and axis in the neck as the head moves forward to play an attacking header in football. **(1)** The system is: atlas and axis (F), weight of the head and ball (L), muscles of the neck (E). **(1)**

5 Second class lever system. **(1)** Award 1 mark for correctly drawn diagram and 1 mark for diagram correctly labelled.

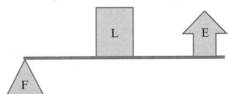

28. Lever systems 2

1 Effort **(1)**
2 A third class lever system can be found at the knee as the leg extends when running. **(1)** The system is: knee (F), weight of the leg (L), quadriceps (E). **(1)**
3 They make it easier to move a heavy load. **(1)**
4 Mechanical disadvantage is where more effort is needed to move a load than the size of the load. **(1)** For example, the effort required to bicep curl 5 kg is greater than 5 kg. **(1)** This is because the effort is closer to the fulcrum than the load being lifted. **(1)**
5 This is a third class lever system. **(1)** Award 1 mark for a correctly drawn diagram and 1 mark for a diagram correctly labelled.

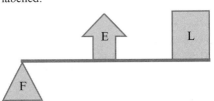

29. Planes and axes of movement 1

1 A = transverse **(1)**; B = sagittal **(1)**
2 Vertical axis **(1)**
3 A plane is an imaginary line that shows the direction of movement allowed in that plane. **(1)** For example, in the sagittal plane the line goes from the front to the back of the body. **(1)** This means backwards and forwards movement is the only direction of movement allowed in this plane. **(1)**
4 Sideways movement **(1)**
5

Plane	Axis
Sagittal	Frontal **(1)**
Frontal	Sagittal **(1)**
Transverse	Vertical **(1)**

30. Planes and axes of movement 2

1 **D** rotation **(1)**
2 The movement is in the transverse plane **(1)** about the vertical axis **(1)**.
3 (a) Frontal plane **(1)**; (b) sagittal axis **(1)**; (c) cartwheel **(1)**
4 The movement is in the sagittal plane **(1)** about the frontal axis **(1)**.

31. Fitness, health, exercise and performance

1 Health is a state of complete emotional, physical and social wellbeing, and not merely the absence of disease and infirmity **(1)**. Fitness is having the ability to meet the demands of the environment **(1)**.
2 Fitness is the ability to meet the demands of the environment **(1)**. Different people will require different levels of fitness depending on what they do on a day-to-day basis **(1)**. For example, a postman who walks several miles a day delivering mail will need to be fit enough to do this; if he isn't, he can't do his job and therefore will not meet the demands of his environment. **(1)**
3 Performance means how well a task is completed. **(1)**
4 **D** It can improve fitness. **(1)**

32. The relationship between health and fitness

1 (a) Exercise **(1)**; (b) fitness **(1)**; (c) Health **(1)**
2 If you exercise regularly **(1)** you can increase your fitness **(1)**. This in turn can lead to an increase in health. **(1)** Regular exercise, good health and fitness will help to improve performance. **(1)**
3 Exercise is an activity that you do in order to improve or maintain your health and fitness. **(1)** If you improve your fitness through regular exercise, this will make you fitter for your activity, which will allow you to perform better. **(1)** For example, a fitter footballer is less likely to get substituted during a game because their performance won't suffer as the game progresses. **(1)**

33. Cardiovascular fitness

1 **C** triathlon **(1)**
2 (i) oxygen **(1)**; exercise **(1)**; tiring **(1)**
   (ii) coronary heart disease **(1)**
3 The long-distance cyclist would need good cardiovascular fitness **(1)** to ensure that their muscles were receiving the necessary oxygen **(1)** for energy production, to allow them to continue to pedal over the duration of the event **(1)**.
4 Although a marathon runner may use speed for a sprint finish or to get past an opponent **(1)**, speed is only used for a short time in the race as the race can last hours **(1)**. Therefore the runner needs good cardiovascular fitness to make sure enough oxygen and nutrients are transported to the working muscles **(1)** to provide the energy required to keep working; otherwise the runner would need to slow down or stop **(1)**.

34. Muscular endurance

1 **C** the ability to exercise the muscles of the body for long periods of time without tiring **(1)**
2 heart **(1)**; oxygen **(1)**; quality **(1)**
3 **A** Long-distance runners require good cardiovascular fitness when they complete a sprint finish. **(1)**
4 Muscular endurance is used for repeated muscle contractions over a long period of time without tiring. **(1)** This means the muscles in the player's arms can keep working, generating enough strength to play hard shots, making it more difficult for the opponent to return them. **(1)** Without high levels of muscular endurance the muscles would be too tired to continue as the match progressed, resulting in a drop in performance levels. **(1)**

35. Flexibility

1 Flexibility is the range of movement possible at a joint. **(1)**
2 **C** sit and reach test **(1)**
3

Performer	How flexibility is used in activity
Sprinter	Flexibility is used at the hip to get a long stride length **(1)** and therefore use as few strides as possible to complete the race in a quicker time **(1)**.
Javelin thrower	Flexibility is used at the shoulder to get full extension at the joint so they can take the arm further back **(1)** so they can throw further **(1)**.

4 (a) A gymnast in a floor routine uses flexibility at the hips when doing the splits to achieve the correct extended shape **(1)** without injury **(1)**.
   (b) A hurdler uses good flexibility at the hip to stretch the leading leg out as far as possible **(1)** so it does not hit the hurdle and cause the hurdler to slow down or fall **(1)**.

36. Reaction time

1 Reaction time is the time it takes to respond to a stimulus **(1)**: for example, close fielding in cricket when the ball comes off the edge of the bat. **(1)**

2

	Order of importance	Justification
1	100 m sprinter **(1)**	Needs to start the race as soon as possible after the gun, even a slight delay at the start could lose the race **(1)**
2	Midfielder **(1)**	Good reaction time could be an advantage as they will be quicker to make decisions about the game, but the game will not necessarily be lost if one player has a poor reaction time **(1)**
3	Gymnast **(1)**	Gymnasts will only need reaction time if they make an error **(1)**

3 The goalkeeper will need good reaction time when a shot on goal has been deflected off a defender. **(1)** This is because the goalkeeper will need to make a fast decision **(1)** to change the direction they were going in to get to the ball in time before it goes in the net **(1)**.

37. Power and speed

1 Speed **(1)**

2

Performer	Example of use of speed by performer in activity	Effect of speed on performance
Rugby player	To sprint past opponents with the ball **(1)**	To successfully score a try as opponents unable to catch them **(1)**
Sprinter	To cover the distance as fast as possible **(1)**	To run faster and beat opponents **(1)**
Long jumper	To run fast in the run-up before the jump **(1)**	To achieve a greater distance in the jump **(1)**

3 **Javelin thrower**: Power is used to bring the arm through quickly while applying as much force as possible to generate more force **(1)** so the javelin goes further **(1)**.

Tennis player: Power is used by the tennis player to hit the ball as hard as possible at speed **(1)**, making it harder for the opponent to return due to the pace at which the ball is travelling **(1)**.

38. Agility

1 A agility **(1)**

2 Squash players need agility to change direction quickly to reach the ball. **(1)** Footballers need to use agility to quickly dodge around the opposition when dribbling the ball. **(1)**

3 A 100 m sprinter does not need to change direction quickly **(1)** as the race is completed in a straight line **(1)**, whereas football players need agility to dodge opponents **(1)** to be able to avoid being tackled **(1)**.

4 A table tennis player will use agility to return a shot that has been placed on the other corner of the table **(1)**. They will need to turn quickly from where they just played a shot to reposition themselves to play the next shot, so they are able to return the ball in time. **(1)**

A gymnast will use agility in their tumbling routine as they move from one position to another. **(1)** They have to change position quickly and with control to maintain the aesthetic quality of the movement. **(1)**

39. Balance and co-ordination

1 A balance **(1)**

2 (a) Dynamic balance **(1)**

(b) Dynamic balance enables the player to keep their centre of mass over their base of support while moving **(1)** so they do not fall over when running with the ball **(1)**.

3 C a movement using two or more body parts at the same time **(1)**

4 A co-ordinated movement will be efficient **(1)**, smooth **(1)** and therefore effective because the technique will be performed correctly. For example, if a tennis player can co-ordinate the body parts to strike the ball in the sweet spot of the racket, the ball will have more pace than if the hand moving the racket arrives a fraction too late to properly connect with the ball. **(1)**

40. Body composition and strength

1 (a) A Both performers use strength in their performance. **(1)**

(b) Both performers use strength in their performance to generate force, the runner uses this force for a good start, the squash player uses it to hit the ball hard **(1)**. Flexibility is important to the runner to increase stride length so they can cover more ground per stride and body composition is important to the squash player to ensure they are not carrying any redundant additional weight due to excess fat **(1)**.

2 B The percentage of body weight that is fat, muscle and bone

3

Who needs it?	Why is it important?	What is the impact of strength on performance?
Weight lifter	To lift heavy weights	The heavier the weight, the more chance of winning **(1)**
Gymnast	To support own body weight	Will score more points as able to hold positions well **(1)**
Rock climbing	To be able to hold own body weight	So they can climb without falling **(1)**

4 The player is being challenged for the ball, so to avoid losing the ball **(1)** he needs to exert a force on his opponent to keep them from knocking him off the ball **(1)**.

41. PARQ and fitness tests

1 Is there any history of coronary heart disease in your family? Yes / No **(1)**; Are you taking any prescription drugs or medication? Yes / No **(1)**

2 To identify potential health issues **(1)**; to base training recommendations on **(1)**

3 To help set targets **(1)**

4 As Michael's coach I could look for the area that needs improving based on the ratings. **(1)** It looks as if Michael has very poor flexibility **(1)** so I would include more flexibility work in his PEP **(1)**.

42. Cardiovascular fitness tests

1 D Harvard step test **(1)**

2 To complete the Cooper 12-minute swim test, you need to work with a partner: one swims, and one counts the number of lengths. **(1)** Swim for 12 minutes. **(1)** Calculate the distance swum based on the length of the pool. **(1)** Use a rating chart to establish your fitness level. **(1)**

3 (a) Example: Hockey player **(1)** as the step test measures cardiovascular fitness and they need this to play well throughout the length of the hockey match. **(1)**

(b) To see if the training improved cardiovascular fitness **(1)**

4 (a) Cooper 12-minute swim **(1)**

(b) Water polo requires endurance while swimming; the Cooper 12-minute swim test is most similar to the event. **(1)**

43. Strength and flexibility tests

1 (a) **Figure 1** – grip dynamometer test **(1)**; **Figure 2** – sit and reach test **(1)**

(b) **Figure 1** – measures strength **(1)**; **Figure 2** – measures flexibility **(1)**

(c) **Figure 1** – rock climbing **(1)**; **Figure 2** – gymnastics **(1)**

2 Sit and reach test measures flexibility in lower back and hamstrings **(1)**; but the butterfly swimmer needs good flexibility at the shoulder **(1)**, so the test is not very relevant to their needs **(1)**.

3 A grip dynamometer is used to test hand and lower arm strength. **(1)** Although both activities use strength this test is more relevant to the tennis player **(1)** because the tennis player needs strong forearms **(1)**, whereas the football performer needs strong legs and core, which this doesn't test **(1)**.

44. Agility and speed tests

1 (a) The 30-metre sprint test is run in a straight line but in the Illinois agility test you need to weave around obstacles. **(1)**

   (b) Agility is the ability to change body position quickly so the Illinois agility test includes something that measures this, i.e. the swerving. **(1)** However, the 30-metre sprint test just measures speed between A and B so you only need to run in a straight line. **(1)**

   (c) (i) 100 m **(1)**; football **(1)** (ii) Football: speed over a short distance is really helpful to beat your opponent to the ball. **(1)** 100 m: because they are clearly fast over 30 m, they may also be fast over 100 m and therefore they could win. **(1)**

2 (a) Illinois agility test **(1)**

   (b) Basketball **(1)**

45. Power and muscular endurance tests

1 (a) To see if the training programme has made any improvement **(1)**

   (b) One-minute press-up test **(1)**

   (c) Because it tests muscular endurance, which is needed as she will use repeated muscle contractions during her match. **(1)** It also focuses on testing upper body muscular endurance, which is relevant as volleyball players use their arms a lot to dig and set the ball **(1)**.

   (d) (i) Vertical jump test **(1)**; (ii) power **(1)**

46. Interpreting fitness test results

1 Correct answers are shown in *italics* in the table.

Test/rating	Before PEP	During PEP				After PEP
	4 Sept	11 Sept	18 Sept	25 Sept	2 Oct	9 Oct
One-minute sit-up	32	34	35	37	38	38
(a) Rating	below average	*below average*	*average*	*average*	*average*	*average*
(b) Vertical jump	48	49	50	54	58	*<60* **(1)**
Rating	average	average	good	good	good	excellent
(c) (ii) Harvard step test	76	78	*80* **(1)**	85	87	*91* **(1)**
(c) (ii) Rating	average	average	*above average* **(1)**	above average	above average	*excellent* **(1)**

   (c) (i) $300 \times 100 = 30\,000$; $30\,000 \div 375 = 80$ **(1)**
   $300 \times 100 = 30\,000$; $30\,000 \div 330 = 91$ **(1)**

   (d) Mason started below average and after 6 weeks reached average **(1)**, which means that there was some improvement but not much **(1)**. Although reaching an average rating, the programme does not appear to have been very effective on improving muscular endurance **(1)**.

47. Progressive overload

1 (a) If you looked at the plans for each session you would see an increase in intensity between the first session and the last. **(1)** If there were a gradual increase between the sessions, this would be progressive overload. **(1)** For example, if the person did 20 sit-ups in week 1, 25 in week 2, 30 in week 3, this would be progressive overload. **(1)**

   (b) If I looked at the results of the first set of tests and compared these to the second **(1)** I would see an increase in fitness test scores in the tests that related to the areas where progressive overload had been applied **(1)**. For example, if in test 1 the person was ranked very poor in

a strength test but then when re-tested achieved a higher ranking **(1)** this could be due to the use of progressive overload when lifting weights **(1)**.

2 A I trained for a few weeks before increasing the amount I lifted and I was careful to only increase it slowly so that I didn't get injured. **(1)**

3 Overtraining is not good for your training programme as it can lead to injury. **(1)** The training programme should be planned so that there are rest days to avoid overtraining. **(1)** However, progressive overload is good for your training programme and should be applied **(1)**, as gradually increasing the intensity will cause your body to adapt to improve your fitness **(1)**.

48. Specificity

1 A matching training to the particular requirements of an activity **(1)**

2 (a) interval training **(1)**   (c) weight training **(1)**
   (b) continuous training **(1)**   (d) fartlek training **(1)**

3 A footballer would focus on varying intensity within fartlek training **(1)**: for example, short sprint maximum intensity then a period of jogging for recovery to match movement on the football pitch **(1)**. A cross-country runner would focus on change of terrain within fartlek training **(1)**: for example, running up and down hills, on the road and through the forest **(1)**.

49. Individual needs and overtraining

1 C ensuring you have sufficient rest before continuing, even if this means following a different training programme than others in your team **(1)**

2 Overtraining **(1)**

3 The principle of individual needs means that you make sure your training is tailored to focus on your needs rather than just the needs of the sport. **(1)** If you focus on your weaknesses and improve these, your performance will improve. **(1)** For example, if I improved my cardiovascular fitness, I would be able to maintain the quality of my performance in matches for longer. **(1)**

4 If you overtrain you increase the risk of injury **(1)** which would have a negative affect as you will have to stop training and you will lose fitness. **(1)**

5 They will have different levels of fitness **(1)** and different levels of ability **(1)** so they need to make sure the programme reflects their individual needs and targets. **(1)**

50. FITT and reversibility

1 F – frequency. The performer would apply frequency by making sure they exercise regularly, and occasionally increasing how often they train so the training continues to have an impact. **(1)**
   I – intensity. The performer would apply intensity by making sure they work hard enough to cause adaptations to improve fitness. **(1)**
   T – time. The performer would make sure they work for long enough in a session, so increasing the time to make the body work harder. **(1)**
   T – type. The performer would make sure their training matches the needs of the sport. **(1)**

2 Specificity **(1)**

3 Student B **(1)** because theirs is the only heart rate that shows any increases during the eight weeks **(1)**.

51. Thresholds of training

1 There is an upper and lower training threshold that we want to keep our heart rate within. **(1)** The section between upper and lower heart rate training threshold values is called our target zone. **(1)** These are used to help us train at the correct intensity to bring about the improvement in fitness that we need for our activity. **(1)**

2 (a) Maximum heart rate is 220 – sister's age 16, therefore 204 bpm **(1)**. The upper limit will be 80% of the maximum heart rate **(1)**. The lower limit will be 60% of the maximum heart rate **(1)**.

(b) They are training for events that have different intensities – one is aerobic, one is anaerobic **(1)**. Therefore they need to train at different thresholds to mirror the requirements of their activity **(1)**. Jed will work at a lower training threshold than Mike **(1)**.

(c)
lower limit	upper limit
220 −18	220 −18
= 202 **(1)**	= 202
80 ×202	90 × 202
÷ 100	÷100
= 161.6	= 181.8
rounded to nearest	rounded to nearest
whole number	whole number
Lower limit:	Upper limit:
80% is 162 bpm **(1)**	90% is 182 bpm **(1)**

52. Continuous training

1 For example: marathon runner **(1)**; hockey player **(1)**; long-distance swimmer **(1)**

2 **C** weight training **(1)**

3 Any form of regular exercise can improve physical, social and mental aspects of health. Continuous training would be seen as a challenge by many if new to training, as you need the emotional willpower to continue to keep running for a continuous period of time. **(1)** If achieved this provides mental benefits of satisfaction and increased self-esteem. **(1)** Many people will also complete continuous training in a club and run with others **(1)**, talking and socialising with other runners and therefore improving their social health **(1)**. Physical health is also improved as continuous training can involve weight-bearing exercises such as running. **(1)** This can strengthen bones and reduce the chance of health issues occurring, such as osteoporosis. **(1)**

4 **A** run for twenty minutes without a break **(1)**; **C** run for ten minutes then cycle for ten minutes without a break **(1)**

53. Fartlek training

1 (a) This area meets the requirements of fartlek training by providing a variety of terrains, which would lead to changes in speed or intensity of work required. **(1)** For example, you could practice running up and down hills, allowing you to vary how hard you are working, as it is hard to run up hill so you would vary your speed. **(1)** The stream, gravel track, woods and grass areas are all different types of surface to run on, giving the opportunity to practice on different terrains. **(1)**

(b) Cross-country runner **(1)**; games player **(1)**

(c) Cardiovascular fitness **(1)**; muscular endurance **(1)**

54. Circuit training

1 (a) and (b) – Answer will depend on training circuit chosen.

(c) It is a good idea to alternate muscle groups being worked because this allows the muscles time for recovery **(1)**, so once rested they can work hard again **(1)**.

2 A station dribbling the ball weaving in and out of cones **(1)** will improve agility **(1)** so the performer will be more able to dodge opponents when running down the court, so they are less likely to lose possession of the ball **(1)**.

55. Interval training

1 (a) Interval training has work and rest periods built into the session (to allow recovery). **(1)**

(b) Although normally used for anaerobic events, interval training can be adapted for use by endurance athletes. **(1)** For example, rather than having short periods of work, the work intervals can be made longer **(1)** and the recovery periods could be active recovery rather than complete rest **(1)**. This will allow the endurance athlete to gradually increase the pace they can run at for a further distance. **(1)**

(c) Examples: 100 m sprinter **(1)**; long jumper **(1)**

(d) To make circuit training more like interval training, there would be a set period of work on each station (for example, 45 seconds) **(1)** followed by a set period of rest (for example 30 seconds) **(1)** before moving on to the next station. This should allow the performer sufficient time for recovery so they can still work at a high intensity. **(1)**

2 Alex's programme will be less intense than Robyn's as they need to have programmes based on their own fitness levels. **(1)** Alex should run shorter distances **(1)** and have longer rests to start with until fitness levels develop **(1)**.

56. Plyometric training

1 **D** volleyball player **(1)**

2 (a) Involves jumping or bounding **(1)**

(b) Plyometric training involves jumping high and fast **(1)** usually over hurdles or onto and off boxes **(1)** with rest periods in between sets **(1)**.

(c) Power **(1)**; strength **(1)**

(d) Volleyball – increases in power will allow the players to jump higher at the net **(1)** to block the ball **(1)**. Sprinter – increased power will allow a more explosive start from the blocks **(1)** to get a better start and therefore be more likely to win **(1)**.

57. Weight/resistance training

1 (a) Weight training involves working with a resistance **(1)**, which can be free weights or fixed weights. You would normally complete a number of repetitions per set and a number of sets **(1)**: for example, 12 repetitions per set and 3 sets **(1)**. Typical exercises would be a biceps curl and a leg press. **(1)**

(b) Muscular strength **(1)**; muscular endurance **(1)**

(c) The amount a person lifts can be altered to match their needs. **(1)** The stronger the individual, the heavier the weights they can lift. **(1)** Performers could use the 1RM (one rep max) to find how much they can lift and then lift a percentage of that, depending on which aspect of strength they wish to increase. **(1)**

(d) An endurance athlete would need to lift light weights many times to increase muscular endurance **(1)** whereas a power athlete would need to lift heavy weights with fewer reps to increase their strength **(1)**.

58. Fitness classes

1 **A** cardiovascular endurance **(1)**

2 A fitness instructor **(1)** can help provide additional motivation **(1)** so they don't give up training **(1)**

3 Pilates develops flexibility and balance. **(1)** Both of these components of fitness are important to a gymnast. **(1)**

4 (a) Spinning **(1)**

(b) Cardiovascular endurance **(1)**

5 It provides continuous activity for 30 to 60 minutes. **(1)**

6 Body pump **(1)**; spinning **(1)**

59. Training methods: pros and cons

1 An advantage of weight training is that it is easy to adapt to improve muscular endurance or strength. **(1)** A disadvantage is it can cause injury if not done properly. **(1)**

2 Although fartlek training mimics the pace required in games activities **(1)** it does not work on skills **(1)**. Circuit training can be adapted to work on both skills and fitness required. **(1)**

3 Advantage: Continuous training will help with their cardiovascular fitness **(1)**, which is useful as it means the player can perform at a higher pace for longer in the game without tiring **(1)**.
Disadvantage: Continuous training is at a constant steady pace **(1)**, which will not help the player work on the speed they need to make darting runs **(1)**.

4 Interval and continuous training can become boring due to their repetitive nature **(1)** compared to fartlek, which gives variety through the change in pace and terrain **(1)**. Therefore a performer may be more inclined to maintain training if they use fartlek. **(1)**

60. The effects and benefits of exercise to the skeletal system

1 (a) (i) Walking (1); (ii) Aerobics (1); tennis (1)
2 A badminton (1)
3 Increased bone density means increased bone strength (1), and therefore the player will have less chance of fractures when tackled (1).
4 They would have stronger bones (1), therefore their bones could withstand a greater force before fracturing or breaking (1) so the weight lifter would be less likely to lose time from training due to injury (1).
5 Less likely to dislocate shoulder joint (1) due to the increased stability of the joint, as the ligaments are more able to hold the bones in place (1)

61. Adaptations to the muscular system

1 C increased muscular atrophy (1)
2 A sprinter would benefit due to increased size (1) and strength of the muscles (1) as this would help them gain more power (1) and therefore sprint faster, increasing their chances of winning (1).
3 Increase in myoglobin stores in the muscles (1)
4 Increase in muscle size (1)
5 C increased cardiovascular fitness (1)

62. Adaptations to the cardiovascular system 1

1 (a) Heart A (1)
  (b) Heart A has a larger muscle wall than B. (1) When you train, your heart has to work harder causing the heart to adapt to the new level of training. (1) This adaptation causes an increase in the size of the muscular wall, which you can see in the picture. (1)
2 (i) Increased strength of heart (1), therefore a reduction in the risk of coronary heart disease (CHD) (1); (ii) drop in resting blood pressure (1) therefore less likely to have a stroke (1).

63. Adaptations to the cardiovascular system 2

1 A more efficient recovery period means that the participant is ready to perform again sooner. (1)
2 Hockey is an endurance activity as it is played over a long time. (1) Therefore it is an aerobic activity that needs high levels of oxygen. (1) The increased number of capillaries will increase the rate of oxygen transport to the working muscles (1), providing the required oxygen for the player to perform effectively over the extended period of time (1).
3 (a) No impact, cardiac output remains the same. (1)
  (b) Your cardiac output at rest will be the same whether you are trained or not, as you do not need a large volume of blood to leave the heart per minute. (1) The values for HR and SV may be different, but the total amount of blood ejected from the heart per minute will be the same. (1)
4 A 65 bpm (1)

64. The effects and benefits of exercise to the respiratory system

1 (a) Increased strength of intercostal muscles (1); increased vital capacity (1)
  (b) (i) Long-distance runner (1) (ii) Alveoli are the site where gaseous exchange takes place in the lungs. (1) If there are more places for gas exchange to take place, more oxygen can be extracted from air. (1) With more oxygen the long-distance runner can increase aerobic energy production and therefore improve their performance. (1)
  (c) (i) Sprinter (1) (ii) They work anaerobically (1) therefore their performance is not dependent on good aerobic fitness (1).
2 Vital capacity is the maximum amount of air that can be forcibly exhaled after breathing in. (1)

65. Injury prevention 1

1 (a)

Activity	Typical risk	How risk may occur
Judo	Bruising (1)	By being thrown to the floor by opponent (1)
Football	Graze/cuts (1)	To shins from opponent's studs (1)
High diving (swimming)	Hitting head on diving board/poolside (1)	Due to mistimed dive (1)
Boxing	Dislocated jaw (1)	From a punch to the face (1)

  (b) Bruno should wear shin pads to protect the skin on the leg (1), so that if he is kicked, the opponent's studs will hit the shin pad (1). This will reduce the impact on Bruno's leg and make it less likely that he will get a cut to the shin (1).
2 (a) Pulled muscle (1); (b) broken tooth (1); (c) cuts (1)

66. Injury prevention 2

1 (a) Horse riding – helmet (1); squash – safety glasses (1); dance – warm up (1); skiing – protective padding (1)
  (b) A helmet cushions the blow to the head if the rider falls, and therefore protects the brain from head injury. (1); squash glasses protect the player from a detached retina as the glasses stop the ball squashing in to the eye. (1); warming up increases muscle elasticity, so the dancer is less likely to pull a muscle. (1); protective padding around pylons means that if a skier skis into them at speed the padding will reduce the impact. (1)
2 Progressive overload (1) means the intensity is increased gradually therefore preventing muscle injury by not putting too much pressure on muscles before they have had time to adapt. (1)

67. Fractures

1 (a) Fracture (1)
  (b) A = Simple (1); B = Compound (1); C = Stress (1); D = Greenstick (1)
  (c) Injury A The bone breaks but does not come through the skin. (1) It can be caused as a result of excessive force on the bone: for example, a forceful tackle in rugby. (1)
  (d) Injury C A small crack forms in the bone. (1) This can be an overuse injury from running on hard surfaces without appropriate rest. (1)
2 B seek medical assistance. (1)

68. Concussion and dislocation

1 (a) D boxer (1)
  (b) Concussion happens when the brain is shaken within the skull, often due to being hit on the head. This might occur in table tennis if a player lets go of the bat, but is more likely to occur in boxing, because their opponent is trying to knock them out (1), so they will be trying to hit them in the head as part of the activity (1). If they are successful the blow to the head could result in slight movement of the brain inside the cranium causing concussion. (1)
2 The ligaments are not able to hold the joint in place (1) so the bone ends that meet at a joint get separated (1).
3 Mistimed catch of ball in netball, so force of pass bends finger back (1)
4 C joint injury (1)

69. Injuries at joints and soft tissue

1 (a) Torn cartilage (1); small tears in the cartilage at the end of the bones (1); pain (1)
  (b) Sprain (1); joint moves out of position when the ligaments get stretched (1); swelling (1)
2 D strain (1)
3 C sudden stopping and turning (1)

4 An abrasion is a cut or graze to the skin. **(1)** It occurs due to friction: for example, if you fall on tarmac during a netball game and skid on the floor. **(1)**

5 Sprains are often caused by forceful twisting. **(1)** Both of these sports involve a lot of pivoting or change of direction **(1)**, which increases the chances of sustaining a sprain compared to other sports where there is not as much pivoting **(1)**.

70 Soft tissue injuries and RICE

1 A Golfer's elbow is a joint injury where the pain is felt on the inside of the elbow. **(1)**

2 Overuse: for example, excessive practice of a particular shot without appropriate rest **(1)**

3 Inflamed tendons **(1)**

4 (a) B RICE **(1)**
   (b) R = Rest **(1)**, I = Ice **(1)**, C = Compression **(1)**, E = Elevation **(1)**

71. Anabolic steroids

1 C to train harder for longer **(1)**

2 Examples: increased aggression **(1)**; acne **(1)**; low sperm count **(1)**

3 Sprinters need to develop strength and power **(1)** whereas long-distance runners focus more on cardiovascular and muscular endurance **(1)**. Anabolic steroids allow the performer to increase strength and power through appropriate training, making them more relevant to the sprinter **(1)**.

4 Taking anabolic steroids is cheating because it gives performers an unfair advantage over their competitors **(1)** by allowing them to train harder and for longer **(1)** so they can build more muscle, increasing their chance of winning **(1)**.

72. Beta blockers

1 Beta blockers are useful to performers who need to be steady and calm when performing **(1)**: for example, in events that require small accurate movements **(1)** such as shooting **(1)**. Other performers in very physical games **(1)**, such as rugby **(1)**, would not want to become too relaxed so would not take beta blockers **(1)**.

2 Poor sleep **(1)**; low blood pressure **(1)**

3 Beta blockers reduce the physical effects of anxiety **(1)**, meaning that in events needing precision the performer can be in more control **(1)**, therefore increasing their accuracy, resulting in a better score **(1)**.

4 Archery **(1)**; diving **(1)**

73. Diuretics

1 (a) Dehydration occurs because more water is lost from the body than taken in. **(1)** The diuretic causes the loss of water. **(1)**
   (b) Kidney failure **(1)** – the performer will need hospital treatment and therefore will not be able to perform **(1)**; feeling nauseous **(1)** – if this happens, the performer will be distracted and not be able to carry out essential techniques or skills effectively, such as failing to tackle an on-coming opponent or dropping a catch, so performance will suffer **(1)**
   (c) Horse racing **(1)** – a jockey may take a diuretic to help them lose weight, to meet the required weight limit **(1)**; sprinting **(1)** – to mask the presence of steroids **(1)**

74. Narcotic analgesics

1 (a) Vomiting **(1)**; loss of concentration **(1)**
   (b) Excessive vomiting can lead to dehydration. **(1)**

2 (a) A tennis player may take narcotic analgesics after they get injured in a game but know they have to play in the next round of the tournament in two days' time. **(1)** This would mask the pain so they could still play. **(1)**
   (b) Narcotic analgesics encourage a person to play with injuries **(1)**, which puts the player at greater risk of having a long-term injury **(1)**.

75. Peptide hormones

1 EPO is more likely to be taken by the long-distance runner because it increases the red blood cell count **(1)**, which means the long-distance runner can carry more oxygen **(1)**. With more oxygen they can maintain a higher pace in the race for longer, as oxygen is used to release energy aerobically **(1)**. It would have the same effect for sprinters, but their race doesn't rely on increased oxygen to complete it, so it doesn't give them the same advantage **(1)**.

2 Heart failure **(1)**; increased viscosity of the blood **(1)**

3 (a) A sprinter might be tempted to take HGH to increase muscle mass **(1)** and to reduce their percentage of body fat **(1)**.
   (b) Heart failure **(1)**; increased risk of arthritis **(1)**

76. Stimulants

1 (a) Stimulants can cause increased anxiety **(1)**, which can lead to depression, impacting on emotional health **(1)**. Stimulants can also cause increased aggression **(1)**, which can damage social health due to the way you behave towards others **(1)**.
   (b) Discovery: if found to be taking performance-enhancing drugs **(1)**, competitors will be banned from competing and have to return medals **(1)**, and will therefore lose face with the public **(1)**.

2 Stimulants can cause an increase in aggression. **(1)** In some sports, such as boxing, aggression is a very important quality to have as the boxer needs to be prepared to become involved in a physical fight with another performer **(1)**. They need to be able to 'attack' their opponent and aggression is needed for this. **(1)**

77 Blood doping

1 D infection **(1)**

2 D long-distance cyclist **(1)**

3 Increased blood thickness **(1)** due to additional blood cells in the blood stream **(1)** that could lead to a blood clot **(1)**.

4 Blood doping is where a performer has blood removed and stored **(1)**, so the body compensates for the loss, replacing the blood over a four- to six-week period **(1)**. Before an event the blood that was removed is injected back into the bloodstream. **(1)**

5 Blood doping is a method because it is a procedure the athlete follows **(1)** rather than something they take **(1)**.

6 The 400 m sprint is an anaerobic activity **(1)**, so the performer would not benefit from increased red blood cells through blood doping **(1)** for oxygen transport **(1)**.

78 Warm up

1 (a)

Phase of warm up	Example activity
Pulse raiser **(1)**	Jog around court, running forwards, backwards, sideways **(1)**
Stretching **(1)**	Stretching hamstrings **(1)**
Drills specific to your activity **(1)**	e.g. for a squash player, fast-paced movement to and from the 'T', shadowing action of playing a shot in each corner **(1)**

   (b) The final phase of the warm up should relate to the activity you are about to take part in **(1)**, so the performer should choose something that relates to their activity. Different activities will have different drills associated with them. **(1)** For example, a badminton player would perform drills involving movement around the court and the practising of badminton strokes, whereas a footballer would use a football to practise skills they would use in the game. **(1)**
   (c) To reduce chance of pulling a muscle **(1)**; to increase blood flow, increasing oxygen availability **(1)**

79. Cool down

1. (a) Do a cool down **(1)**
   (b) There are two phases to a cool down. There should be a slow reduction in the intensity of activity **(1)**: for example, reducing intensity to a slow jog or walk **(1)**. After this the performer should stretch the muscles that have been in use during the main session **(1)**: for example, runners would focus on the leg muscles **(1)**.
   (c) It should gradually decrease. **(1)**
   (d) To slowly return the body to its resting state **(1)** To slowly bring the heart rate down **(1)** To avoid blood pooling **(1)** To remove lactate/lactic acid **(1)**.

80. Component 1 – Extended answer question 1

Long-term training can cause the body to adapt, provided the training is appropriate and the correct principles of training have been applied.

An adaptation of regular training on the skeletal system is an increase in bone density. This makes the bones stronger and more able to cope with increased resistance, so in their basketball games if the players fall or receive a knock on court it is less likely to cause an injury to the skeleton. Not only do the bones increase in strength, but so too do the ligaments, tendons and muscles. With stronger ligaments the players' joints are less likely to dislocate. For example, when making a sudden stop and change of direction, either to dodge an opponent or to intercept a pass, a non-secure joint could dislocate, but with increased stability of the joint due to regular training this is less likely to happen. The impact of this is that injury is less likely, and therefore the player can continue to train and improve.

Another adaptation of regular training is increased size in the muscle, or muscular hypertrophy. This means the muscle can generate more strength or power. This will be useful to the basketball players when they need to jump to take a shot or a rebound, as more power will mean greater height so they can get the ball before their opponent. While these effects are positive, if a performer trains too much this can cause overuse injuries, such as shin splints to the skeleton making further weight-bearing exercise painful. This would be a negative impact on the skeletal system and on performance, as the performer would have to rest to allow the body time to recover. Similarly, lifting excessive weights could cause muscles to tear, again resulting in injury. Therefore it is essential that training is well thought-out and planned, so that the positive impact can be achieved without risk to health and future performance.

81. Component 1 – Extended answer question 2

Circuit training is a flexible method of training that you can use to develop skill and fitness, as you can have different activities at each station. By altering the intensity of the work at each station you can also work at your own level. This means that Mrs Rana could organise the session so that each player is working at a different station, at the pace that is right for them. For example, one could be doing shuttle runs to increase speed on court, while another could be practicing shooting. This would be a good choice, as it would allow Mrs Rana to tailor the stations to particular requirements. For example, a goal shooter could practice shooting, whereas the wing attack could practice quickly moving off the spot in different directions, to mirror movement at a centre pass.

However, the use of circuit training also has disadvantages. If players are working independently on each station it doesn't allow them to develop the team aspect of the game, such as strategies for back line passes. So while they may be increasing fitness and some aspects of skill required for the game, players would not develop strategies and tactics, nor would they develop their skills under pressure. For example, while a skill of dodging could be improved using cones to indicate when to stop and change direction, this will be much easier than a game situation if it is unopposed. Therefore while there are advantages to circuit training, it would not seem to be adequate for all training needs, so should be used with another method to ensure the players develop all aspects of game play.

82. Improving health

1. **D** complete emotional, social and physical wellbeing **(1)**
2. 1 = Design **(1)**; 2 = Monitor **(1)**
3. If you are unsure why you are training you will not be able to effectively design the programme **(1)**, and therefore you will be unlikely to see any increase in health **(1)**.
4. If you follow the proper procedure, the programme you design should reflect the aspect of health you want to improve. **(1)** Even if you don't develop it exactly right, due to the monitoring you will notice this. **(1)** Therefore as part of the evaluation of the session you can modify the programme **(1)** to get the health benefits you want **(1)**.

83. Physical health

1. (a) Less likely to suffer from osteoporosis **(1)**; less likely to become obese **(1)**
   (b) Less likely to suffer from osteoporosis due to increased bone strength **(1)** as a result of regular weight-bearing exercise **(1)**; less likely to become obese due to additional use of calories burned **(1)** during aerobic exercise **(1)**.

2.

Effect	Physical health benefit
Reduction in resting blood pressure	Reduction in likelihood of suffering from coronary heart disease **(1)**
Increased bone strength	Reduced chances of suffering from osteoporosis **(1)**
Weight loss when overweight	Less likely to become obese, therefore less strain on the heart **(1)**

84. Emotional health

1. **C** competition **(1)**
2. They would be playing in a team against other teams. **(1)** They could also be fighting for their place in the team. **(1)**
3. (a) relieve **(1)**; emotional **(1)** (b) aesthetic **(1)** (c) serotonin **(1)**; feel good **(1)**
4. By practising more when you take part your skill level will improve. **(1)** If you are good at something it makes you feel good about yourself, which improves your self-esteem. **(1)**

85. Social health

1. Making new friends **(1)**; by joining a club, he will meet new people and can make friends with them **(1)**. Learning to co-operate with others **(1)**; through playing with others and working with them, he will become a better team player **(1)**.
2. The children will learn how to play with each other **(1)** – for example, taking it in turns to bowl – and therefore they will develop co-operation skills **(1)**. While taking part in the activity they will also make new friends **(1)** by socialising with others **(1)**.
3. By joining a club and swimming or running with others Desmond would come into contact with other people. **(1)** Through mixing socially with others **(1)** and developing friendships he would improve his social health **(1)**.

86. Lifestyle choices 1

1. (a) They make time for rest from school work **(1)** and they are being active **(1)**.
   (b) By choosing to be active on a regular basis they will improve their physical health. **(1)** This is because the activity will reduce cholesterol build-up **(1)**, reducing the risk of high blood pressure as they get older **(1)**.
2. If you eat more than the recommended daily amount without exercising to compensate **(1)** for this you will put on weight **(1)**. If you continue to do this you can become obese **(1)**, which can then increase your risk of other health issues such as type 2 diabetes or stroke. **(1)**

87. Lifestyle choices 2

1. (a) Cardiovascular system (1); respiratory system (1)
   (b) (i) Performance-enhancing drugs are illegal for sports people as they improve performance. (1). (ii) They will not improve performance, and therefore will not give an athlete an unfair advantage. (1)
   (c) Smoking can cause lung cancer. (1) This is because the smoke contains carcinogens. (1)
   (d) Drinking alcohol can cause liver damage (1) such as cirrhosis (1). This is because normal liver tissue is replaced by scar tissue, which causes liver cells to die, making it harder for the liver to function. (1)
2. Drinking alcohol (1)

88. Sedentary lifestyle 1

1. When a person has little or no physical activity (1)
2. (i) Osteoporosis (1); (ii) depression (1); (iii) type 2 diabetes (1)
3. A sedentary lifestyle would lead to a drop in cardiovascular fitness (1) due to loss of cardiac function: for example, a drop in stroke volume (1). Having less oxygen circulated per beat would reduce the ability to work aerobically (1).
4. Obesity levels for girls rise as they get older. (1) The group with the highest obesity levels according to the data is 11–12-year-old boys. (1)

89. Impact of a sedentary lifestyle on weight

1. (a) Obese, overfat, overweight (2)
   (b) If you are obese this can lead to a number of health issues, such as type 2 diabetes and heart disease. It can also reduce life expectancy. (1) If you are overfat, this is still a health issue as it can lead to increased blood pressure and high cholesterol. (1) Being overweight might be nothing to do with having extra fat; you could be overweight because you have dense bones or have a lot of muscle mass, so this need not be dangerous to health at all (1).
2. Sustained activity will use calories that would otherwise be stored in the body. (1) Therefore if you exercise regularly, you will put on less weight than if you didn't exercise at all. (1)

90. Diet and energy balance

1. (a) Carbohydrates, fats, proteins (1) minerals, vitamins, water, fibre (1)
   (b) A = carbohydrates (1); B = proteins (1); C = fats (1)
2. When we eat we take in calories that can be used as energy. (1) We need to make sure the amount we eat matches our energy requirements (1), otherwise consuming too many calories would lead to weight gain, or consuming too few calories would lead to weight loss (1).

91. Macronutrients

1. Carbohydrates, protein, fat (1)
2. D to help with muscle growth as a result of training adaptations (1)
3. One athlete could be a man, the other a woman; the recommended intake is less for women than it is for men. (1) The athletes could do different sports and therefore have different energy demands. (1)
4. Carbohydrates are used for energy. (1) Without sufficient energy we would not be able to be active. (1) Proteins are needed for growth and repair of body cells. (1) Without protein we would not be able to repair damaged muscle cells, which would prevent us from remaining active. (1)

92. Micronutrients

1. Vitamins, minerals (1)
2. (a) A micronutrient is something that you should eat which is good for the body (nutrient) (1), but that is only needed in small quantities on a daily basis (micro) (1).
   (b) (i) Answers are given in column 2 of the table. (ii) Suggested answers are given in column 3 of the table.

Types of micronutrient		Examples of each type of micronutrient
1	Vitamins (1)	1 Vitamin C (1)
		2 Vitamin D (1)
2	Minerals (1)	1 Iron (1)
		2 Calcium (1)

   (c) Vitamin C can reduce the risk of heart disease if correct quantities are taken. (1) Vitamin D encourages the absorption of calcium to help strengthen bones. (1) Iron is an important part of haemoglobin; without sufficient iron you could become anaemic and not be able to transport oxygen effectively. (1) Calcium is needed for healthy bones, so lack of calcium can lead to osteoporosis. (1)

93. Optimum weight

1. Ideal weight for an individual based on certain physiological factors (1), such as height (1)
2. Your height (1) will affect your optimum weight. The taller you are the more you will weigh. (1) Sex (1) – men tend to have more muscle than women, and therefore a man of the same height as a woman is likely to weigh more (1). Bone structure (1) – the more dense your bones, the heavier you will be (1). Muscle girth (1) – the more muscular you are, the more you will weigh (1).
3. A jockey's optimum weight will be different from a high jumper's. Jockeys need to be light (1) and therefore they tend to be short compared to other sports performers (1). In high jumping it is an advantage to be tall (1), which will increase weight, so high jumpers tend to be tall but with limited muscle girth compared to other performers in other activities (1).
4. The optimum weight for a rugby prop would be more than for a rugby winger (1), as the prop needs more mass for their role (1), whereas the player on the wing will need to be quicker, more agile and therefore likely to weigh less (1).

94. Dietary manipulation

1. Changing diet to maximise the food sources for optimum performance for an event (1)
2. C long-distance cyclist (1)
3. (a) Carbohydrate loading is a strategy to increase carbohydrate stores in the body (1), which increases glycogen stores for an event (1), so that more energy can be produced quickly for sustained physical activity in endurance events such as triathlons (1).
   (b) 1 to 4 days (1)
4. Sweating, due to increased temperature through physical activity, can cause dehydration (1), leading to dizziness and nausea, (1) leading to a drop in performance levels (1).

95. Classification of skills 1

1. Open – closed (1); basic (simple) – complex (1); low organisation – high organisation (1)
2. C receiving a serve in tennis (1)
3. A closed skill is one that is not affected by the environment. (1)
4. A vault in gymnastics is a closed skill. This is because the gymnast decides when to start (1), and therefore they can pre-plan the vault (1). As the opposition does not have direct contact, the skill does not need to be adapted. (1)

96. Classification of skills 2

1. It does not require much thought or decision making. (1)
2. C laying up a shot in basketball (1)
3. Complex skills are difficult (1); they need the performer to process a lot of information when carrying them out (1).
4. At the complex end of the continuum (1), as there is a lot of decision making (1) about when to run, pass and let go of the baton (1)
5. A tennis serve is an example of a low organisation skill (1) because it can be easily broken down (1) into separate phases for practice: for example, ball toss and throwing of racket (1).

97. Massed and distributed practice

1 Distributed practice (1)
2 The task is complex and could be dangerous. (1) If they did massed practice they could get too tired (1) and make mistakes that could lead to injury (1).
3 (a) An advantage of massed practice is that it helps to groove the correct technique. (1) A disadvantage of massed practice is that it can be boring. (1)
   (b) An advantage of distributed practice is that it can maintain motivation. (1) A disadvantage of distributed practice is that it can be time-consuming, as it takes longer to learn a skill. (1)

98. Fixed and variable practice

1 **D** practice structured so the skill is repeated in an unchanging situation (1)
2 When the same skill is repeated but in different situations (1)
3 If the athlete were learning a sprint start (1) they would practise on the track with starting blocks (1) to make the practice as similar to the event as possible (1).
4 Variable practice is used with open skills (1): for example, a return of service in tennis (1), so the performer gets used to returning lots of different types of serve and is prepared for this in a game (1).
5 Dribbling is an open skill (1), and therefore it is important to organise the practice structure so that the skill can be developed in changing situations (1). This means the coach should use variable practice (1).

99. Values of goal setting 1

1 It helps you to plan your training by giving specific focus. (1) It helps you develop your ability by focusing on weaknesses. (1) It helps you maintain training by motivating you to continue to work towards the goal or target. (1)
2 To move up to the second team by the second half of the season (1)
3 (a) Decrease time to 14.0 s (1)
   (b) Increase high jump to 1 m 55 cm (1)
   (c) Get into the first team (1)
   (d) Increase total goals scored over next six games to 12 (1)
   (e) Increase their personal best tariff score to 5.0 (1)

100. Values of goal setting 2

1 (a) To take almost 2 seconds off their 100 m time within two weeks (1) would be too difficult to achieve. It may be possible over a longer period. (1)
   (b) It would be too big a jump to go from fifth to first place (1) in a competition where there will be very good performers as at county level (1).
   (c) This would mean a huge increase in the number of goals scored (1), needing at least 3 goals per match (1).
   (d) An increase of 1.5 to achieve a perfect score would be very difficult (1), especially by their next competition (1).
2 Play for the second team by the end of next season (1)
3 By setting a measureable goal (1) they can monitor progress (1). Knowing their training is working will motivate them to continue with it. (1)

101. Visual and verbal guidance

1 Demonstrations (1) must be accurate (1) so that the performer learns the technique correctly (1).
2 As they are beginners they have no idea of what the skill should look like. (1) By visually showing the performer the technique they can form a mental picture of the skill (1) that they can then reproduce based on this image (1).
3 (a) When the players were experienced (1): for example, reviewing footwork at half time during a netball match (1).
   (b) Advantage: instructions can be given quickly (1); disadvantage: can be difficult to understand if given too much information (1)

102. Manual and mechanical guidance

1 **A** using an aid to help a performer learn a skill (1)
2 Mechanical guidance involves the use of an aid , whereas manual does not (1).
3 Mechanical (1)
4 (a) Manual (1)
   (b) The coach physically supports or moves the performer (1) to help them get the correct feel of the movement (1).
5 If the children are not strong swimmers they will need some support while learning so they do not drown. (1) As there is a class of 12 the coach could not support each one individually at the same time. (1) Therefore the coach will use floats or harnesses to keep the swimmers afloat while they practice parts of their technique. (1)

103. Types of feedback

1 **B** information given to the performer during performance
2 Elite performers do not need extrinsic feedback because the coach is dealing with experienced performers (1) who can detect their own faults and correct them (1).
3 Terminal feedback would be given at the end of the skill (1): for example, after a high jump attempt (1).
4 The coach should think about how skillful the performer is (1) and the type of skill being taught (1), because if the performer is a beginner they will need a lot of extrinsic feedback (1), and if it is a fast paced skill they should provide feedback after the skill is completed, terminally (1).
5 The group receiving extrinsic feedback is the highest scoring group. This shows that, as all groups are beginners, this is the most effective form of feedback. (1) The group reliant on intrinsic feedback on its own seems to be the least effective overall, as the fewest baskets were scored using this form of guidance. (1) Although overall the extrinsic feedback group scored more than the intrinsic feedback group, you can see that with more practice the intrinsic feedback group are showing a greater rate of improvement (1), demonstrating that over time this type of feedback would also be effective (1).

104. Mental rehearsal

1 **C** it allows the performer to think about completing the action correctly. (1)
2 Going through a movement in your head before physically performing it (1)
3 A player would perform mental rehearsal as part of a warm up before competing. (1)
4 In breaks in play, e.g. before the game or at half time (1) but also prior to an important free kick, or if awarded a penalty (1), the striker would mentally rehearse seeing themselves scoring the goal before actually taking the penalty (1).
5 Some activities are continuous, for example, games (1), therefore the players do not get a lot of time to mentally rehearse, because if they did stop to do this they would lose possession of the ball (1). However, other activities such as athletics, for example, the high jump and long jump, contain discrete skills (1) that are not impacted on by others, therefore there is time to mentally rehearse before completing the jump (1).

105. Socio-economic groups

1 (a) Students draw their own bar chart (2)

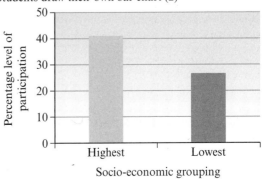

(b) Lack of money among lower socio-economic group **(1)** therefore less to spend on leisure activities **(1)**

2   If you are in a job where you are paid a lot of money due to it being a high socio-economic group **(1)** you will have more money to spend on sport – for example, on sports equipment or travel**(1)**. Therefore your choices will not be as limited as for someone from a lower socio-economic group **(1)** and you are more likely to find a sport that interests you and participate in it. **(1)**

3   The Government spends millions on the NHS. **(1)** Therefore, as physical activity can help to increase health **(1)**, the Government wants to encourage participation in the hope of increasing the health of the nation to reduce costs **(1)**.

106. Gender and age groups

1   (a) C fitness and conditioning **(1)**
    (b) Fitness and conditioning is considered a socially acceptable activity for women. **(1)**

2   Women may have less time for sport **(1)** because traditionally they look after the children as well as work **(1)**. Women generally earn less than men **(1)** and therefore do not have as much money to spend on sport **(1)**.

3   Adults have reduced access to sport **(1)** and they may have to join a club if they want to play **(1)**, whereas when at school sport is available through PE lessons or after-school clubs **(1)**.

107. Ethnicity and disability groups

1   The general trend is an increase in participation from 2006 to 2015 **(1)**. However, the trend over the last year of the graph has been downwards **(1)**, as rates have dropped from 1.69 million to 1.56 million. The steepest drop was in the six-month period between April 2014 and October 2014 **(1)**, so although still dropping in April 2015 the drop was much less, potentially indicating a levelling out in terms of participation over the next year **(1)**.

2   There could be a lack of availability or access. **(1)** For example, a wheelchair user may want to play basketball, but may not live close enough to a sports facility that offers this wheelchair activity. **(1)** Or this could be due to stereotyping **(1)** For example, the person may feel uncomfortable going to a local sports centre to use the gym due to the reaction of others. **(1)**

3   Stereotyping in sport is where we assume that certain groups of people will all have the same skills and abilities. **(1)** For example, because Usain Bolt is good at sprinting, a stereotypical view would be that all Jamaicans would be good at sprinting **(1)**. This might mean that anyone from that ethnic group would be encouraged to participate in sprinting rather than another activity **(1)**.

108. Commercialisation, the media and sport

1   Selling an event, product or service for profit **(1)**
2   Sport **(1)**
3   Through sponsorship **(1)**; by selling the right to televise an event **(1)**
4   The broadcasting viewing levels show that billions of people watch the Olympics **(1)** therefore all of these people will see the sponsors name making the brand more familiar so viewers are more likely to purchase it **(1)**, increasing profits for the company **(1)**.
5   All three need each other to provide the money they need to develop further **(1)**. For example, sport receives money from commercial companies that pay to advertise their product **(1)**; the media broadcast sport worldwide so it is seen by a larger audience **(1)**; people like to watch sport, making the media popular, so they receive money from companies for 'air time' to advertise in the breaks in play **(1)**.

109. The advantages of commercialisation

1   The huge number of viewers means that the sponsor's products were seen by 90 per cent of the UK population **(1)**, thus increasing the awareness of their product, as so many

people will have seen their name when they watched the TV **(1)**. This would increase sales. **(1)**

2   This time slot will have been chosen as it would be when most people in the UK could watch the event **(1)**, because most people would not be out, at work or asleep **(1)** and therefore it would get the maximum possible number of viewers in the UK **(1)**.

3   The performer can get large sums of money **(1)**, which means that they can train full-time **(1)**, and therefore they can increase training and focus on becoming the best at their sport **(1)**.

4   For football spectators, there will be more money paid to the teams **(1)**, which means that clubs can afford better players **(1)**, making the teams even more entertaining to watch **(1)**.

110. The disadvantages of commercialisation

1   Breaks in play for advertising proposes **(1)** will disturb the natural flow of the game **(1)**; minority sports not shown by media **(1)** reducing interest in these sports, leading to a decrease in grassroots participation **(1)**

2   Sports performers do not want to be seen to support something unethical **(1)** such as a clothing manufacturer that relies on child labour **(1)**, as this would reflect negatively on the performer and is not something they should be encouraging **(1)**.

3   Spectators should experience high subscription costs for TV sports channels **(1)** and have to pay for particular popular events through pay per view **(1)** – needing to pay again for certain matches/events **(1)**. If their sport is not popular it is less likely to be shown on the TV. **(1)**

4   If the performer does something to make them a bad role model **(1)**, such as taking performance-enhancing drugs **(1)**, the performer's popularity will drop so fewer people will buy the sponsorship company's products **(1)**.

111. Sporting behaviour

1   A time wasting **(1)**
2   Sportsmanship **(1)**
3   Bending the rules **(1)** to gain an unfair advantage over the opposition **(1)**: for example, a player might not admit if they were the last to touch the ball before it went out, so they could get the throw in **(1)**
4   Elite sports men and women are role models to those who play the sport at grassroots **(1)**. This means the elite performers' behaviour is likely to influence the behaviour of others. **(1)** If they behave well on the pitch, this reinforces the positive values of sport and encourages grassroots players to behave in the same way. **(1)**

112. Deviance in sport

1   (a) To put the opponent off so they can beat them **(1)**
    (b) Biting is against the rules of the sport, and therefore is deviant behaviour. **(1)** It is not allowed in the sport because it will cause physical harm to an opponent **(1)** and is considered assault **(1)**.
2   For fame associated with winning **(1)**; for the increase in sponsorship deals associated with being the best **(1)**
3   Campaigns such as 100% Me are necessary because not all sports performers demonstrate these values **(1)**. Therefore, campaigns promote the positive values of sporting achievement **(1)** by using good role models **(1)** in order to reinforce the correct sporting values for those just taking up the sport **(1)**.

113. Component 2 – Extended answer question 1

SMART stands for specific, measurable, achievable, realistic and time bound.

Specific means that Dimitri should set clear goals that he wants to achieve; in the question it says he wants to improve his performance, but this is not specific enough. If he had such a loose target he would be unlikely to improve, therefore to be effective the SMART principles need to be applied. For example, he might set a specific goal to reduce the number of unforced errors he makes in a match. By setting a specific goal Dimitri will have a clear focus on what he wants to achieve and therefore can set about doing that. This would help him tailor his training sessions so that he practices his skills, but also the unforced errors could be due to lack of cardiovascular fitness, so he could devise an interval training programme to improve his badminton fitness. Interval training would be appropriate as badminton involves lots of short, intense movements on the court, with short breaks. Dimitri also needs to set measurable targets. For example, if he counted the number of errors he normally made, e.g. serving out, and then set a target to reduce this by five he would be able to see if his training was working.

Dimitri's goals need to be achievable and realistic; if they are not he will become demotivated and give up trying to achieve his goal. Similarly, although they should be time bound, this time frame also has to be achievable. There is no point trying to improve too quickly. Apart from the potential for injury through overtraining, if the deadline comes and improvement has not been made, again this will be demotivating and may lead to Dimitri giving up.

114. Component 2 – Extended answer question 2

Personal factors such as age, disability, gender, socio-economic group and ethnicity can impact on someone's level of participation in physical activity and sport. For example, nationally men participate in sport more than women, and those with a disability participate the least. This is mainly due to the barriers to participation faced by different groups. For example, adapted facilities need to be available for disability sport; without these, people with disabilities will not be able to access the sport, and people without a disability will have more opportunity to play. These factors impact not only on the amount you participate but also on the activities you choose to participate in. Those from a lower socio-economic group would have less money to spend on expensive membership fees or equipment needed for some sports, such as golf. Therefore they would be less likely to participate in these activities, choosing something less expensive to play, such as football. There are always exceptions to the rule, but generally those from lower socio-economic groups will opt for cheaper sports. Another example is that women are more likely to participate in aerobics than men as aerobics is seen as a socially acceptable activity for women to participate in but less so for men, who are expected to participate in more aggressive or competitive sports, such as rugby or boxing. However, we have seen more recently a change in attitudes. It is becoming more acceptable for women to do any sport they want: for example, women are now allowed to compete in boxing matches. So gender stereotyping is having less of an impact at elite level. The elite female boxers in the media are role models for girls to follow, which should slowly increase the number of girls taking up boxing, so reducing the impact of this personal factor.

115. Multiple choice questions

1   **A** vitamins **(1)**
2   **D** increased number of red blood cells **(1)**
3   **B** prevents injury **(1)**
4   **A** increased heart rate **(1)**
5   **D** Vasodilation is the widening of blood vessels supplying the working muscles. **(1)**
6   **C** Diuretics can be used to remove other drugs from the body. **(1)**

116. Short answer questions

1   Target zone 220 minus the age of the athlete **(1)**; The lower limit is 60% of the total **(1)**; The upper limit is 80% of the total **(1)**
2   Vertical jump test **(1)** Stand side on to wall both feet flat on floor, reach up and mark with chalk **(1)**; jump as high as possible mark the board with chalk **(1)**; measure the distance and compare to national ratings chart **(1)**.
3   Anaerobic **(1)**, as it is a short explosive activity **(1)** that does not require oxygen to complete the skill **(1)**

4   Progressive overload is gradually increasing the intensity of the workload. **(1)** This increases fitness but avoids injury. **(1)**
5   Week 1 he could complete 3 sets of 8 reps of 5 kg. **(1)** Week 3 he could complete 3 sets of 10 reps of 5 kg. **(1)**
6   M stands for measurable, so that it is possible to see any changes in performance. **(1)** If they are improving this will motivate them therefore they will be more likely to continue to train. **(1)**

117. Use of data questions

1   (a) Speed – Katya **(1)**; strength – Katya **(1)**; flexibility – Dave **(1)**
    (b)

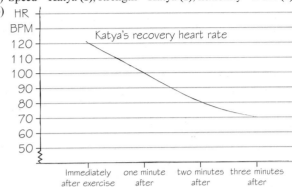

118. Extended answer questions 1

Plan:
*   Benefits of each type of drug – (knowledge) Which of the two types of performer would benefit from the advantage and how – (application)
*   Evaluation – (judgment, which drug gives the greatest benefit to which athlete)

Possible answer:

EPO stands for Erythropoietin. It is a type of peptide hormone that can increase the red blood cell count of the athlete. This means that the athlete can get an increased supply of oxygen to their working muscles. Oxygen is used to help release energy, so the more oxygen available, the more energy can be released aerobically. The power athlete does not have the time to use oxygen to release energy during their event, so although an oxygen supply is important, this is needed after the event in recovery. The endurance athlete, however, needs a constant supply of oxygen as they work aerobically for most of their event, therefore EPO would be very beneficial to them, providing them with more oxygen so they can maintain the quality of their run for longer before slowing down due to fatigue.

Diuretics increase urination, and therefore increase the removal of fluids from the body. This can be used for rapid weight loss or to mask other performance-enhancing drugs. The rapid weight loss is unlikely to be particularly useful to either an endurance athlete or a power athlete, but any athlete could benefit from the masking properties of diuretics if they were taking another form of performance-enhancing drug.

To conclude, neither of the drugs offer the power athlete direct advantage for performance in their event. They would be more likely to take anabolic steroids to help them train for longer and build muscle mass. The endurance athlete, however, would gain a direct advantage from EPO and this would be one of the drugs they would be tested for in a random drugs test at elite level.

119. Extended answer questions 2

Plan:
*   Advantages of weight training – (knowledge)
*   Disadvantages of weight training – (knowledge)
*   Advantages of weight training for footballers – (application)
*   Disadvantages of weight training for footballers – (application)
*   Advantages of other training methods for footballers – (application)
*   Disadvantages of other training methods for footballers – (application)
*   Evaluation – would weight training be most appropriate, if so why?

Possible answer:

Weight training is the perfect training method for improving a player's muscular strength or muscular endurance. Both of these aspects of fitness are required by footballers. When muscular strength is combined with speed it generates power, another important component of fitness for the footballer, so another good reason to develop strength through weight training. Weight training is often carried out indoors and can accommodate a relatively large number of people in a small space, so the team could all train together but still set individual targets for the number of repetitions and sets to complete and the weight to lift, depending on their individual needs.

Other methods of training could also be used as they also have benefits. For example, the footballers would benefit from circuit training, as the use of different stations would allow them to work on aspects of technique as well as fitness. Fartlek training would also be beneficial as this can be adapted to match the changing pace of the game.

Plyometric training could be used to help increase the players' power. This would help them increase the height they could jump to beat an opponent when heading a ball to clear it. The players could use more than one training method within a week so they could benefit in different ways. This would provide variation and opportunity to work on different components of fitness that are relevant to football: for example, they could alternate between weight sessions and fartlek training sessions.

Weight training may not be the most appropriate method because it does not allow for skill development or improvement in cardiovascular fitness, which are two essential aspects required by a footballer to maintain the required work rate throughout the match. To conclude, I think I would use cross training and incorporate several different types of training sessions within the teams' overall training programme. I would use fartlek training to improve their cardiovascular fitness, circuit training to focus on skill development, and weight training or plyometric training to enhance their power, making them stronger and more powerful on the ball so that shots are more difficult to stop and long passes are more likely to reach their intended target.

120. Timed test 1

Note: These are sample answers; other responses are sometimes possible.

1 (a) **B** cartwheel
   (b) **D** the ability to meet the demands of the environment
   (c) **C** overtraining
   (d) **C** It increases the amount of blood flowing to the working muscles.
   (e) **B** increased heart rate
   (f) **C** It is caused by anaerobic respiration and is paid back after exercise.
   (g) **B** It increases the ability to train harder.
   (h) **D** flexion, extension

2 Bones are placed over vital organs so the bone stops the vital organ getting damaged. For example, the ribs would protect a rugby player's heart and lungs when he is tackled and falls heavily on the ground.

3 The quadriceps are at the front of the thigh. Their role is to extend the leg at the knee. The pectoralis major are across the chest. Their role is adduction of the upper arm at the shoulder.

4 The ankles are plantar-flexed due to the action of the gastrocnemius. This muscle is contracting while the tibialis anterior is relaxing. The tibialis anterior is the other part of the antagonistic pair. The legs are straight, but the hip is flexed due to the action of the hip flexors, which allows him to bend at the hip to put his legs in front of him. The muscle working antagonistically with the hip flexors is the gluteus maximus.

5 **A** left atrium; **B** left ventricle

6 Platelets in the blood form a clot at the injury or break in the skin. This prevents further bleeding so the performer can return to the game.

7 The alveoli provide a large surface area and are thin-walled therefore allow gases to pass through easily.

8 Cardiac output increases from resting value by increasing heart rate and stroke volume so that there is an increased blood flow to transport the additional oxygen being breathed in by the respiratory system.

9 An advantage is that energy can be released quickly as oxygen is not needed to break down carbohydrate. A disadvantage is that, without oxygen, lactic acid will accumulate which will tire the muscles due to the increased acidity in the tissue.

10 Immediate effects: increased depth of breathing; increased oxygen debt
   Effect of regular participation: increased vital capacity

11 The lines on the graphs for both heart rate (HR) and breathing rate (BR) are increasing. HR increases at a much steeper rate than BR, so seems to be more affected by the increase in exercise. If the person is 20 years old, as the intensity of the exercise increases to vigorous, the performer moves into their anaerobic training zone as their HR has gone over 160 bpm.

12 (a) Second class lever
   (b) (Student sketch) Load is in the middle, effort pointing up at one end, fulcrum at the other.

13 Figure 8 as this is a third class lever system and the point of effort is closer to the fulcrum than the load.

14 (a) Flexibility
   (b) Sprinter: increase stride length therefore can cover ground more rapidly; hurdler: achieve efficient shape over the hurdle therefore doesn't need to slow down as much when clearing the hurdle
   (c) Agility. This is the ability to change direction of body position quickly with control. The hurdler needs to do this to clear the hurdles but the 100 m sprinter just runs in a straight line.

15 Muscular endurance involves repeated contraction of specific muscles during an activity without tiring, whereas cardiovascular fitness means the ability to exercise the entire body for long periods of time without tiring. Therefore both need to work for long periods of time without tiring but one is about specific muscles while the other is about the whole body.

16 Harvard step test: cardiovascular fitness; hockey
   Vertical jump test: power; high jump
   One-minute sit-up test: muscular endurance; rowing

17 She would use it to establish the baseline fitness of her players so that she could establish their strengths and weaknesses, which she could then use to focus on in training, increasing their fitness, e.g. working on their agility, which could improve their ability to dodge the opposition.

18 Wear a gum shield to protect your teeth from being knocked out by a hockey stick. Check the pitch for things like broken glass before you start to play so no cuts when tackled in rugby. Have an official to make sure there is no dangerous play.

19 Increase blood flow so more oxygen available for working muscles; to increase the elasticity of muscles so less chance of injury; to mentally get ready for the activity.

20 This is because it is still a way of artificially enhancing performance that gives an unfair advantage to the performer but also carries serious health risks.

21 The long-term training effects are those that happen to the body as a result of regular training; they are the adaptations that the body makes to cope with the extra exercise. One effect is cardiac hypertrophy. This means the muscular wall of the heart has increased in strength so it can contract more forcibly. This is good for the performer because this means their stroke volume will increase (the amount of blood ejected from the heart per beat), which allows them to increase blood flow around the body during exercise so more oxygen can be transported to the working muscles so the performer can work aerobically for longer, reducing the effects of fatigue. Capillarisation is a result of regular training. This means more capillaries will open to allow better blood flow carrying

oxygen and nutrients to the muscles and taking away lactate and carbon dioxide. Quicker lactate breakdown due to increased oxygen delivery will reduce muscle fatigue; again this is very important to the endurance athlete due to the length of their event, which could be hours if it is a marathon. These effects are particularly important to a long-distance runner as they all lead to increased oxygen delivery to the working muscles and increased removal of carbon dioxide. This means the performer will be able to utilise fat stores rather than rely on carbohydrate for his energy, meaning that their energy stores will last longer so they can continue in the race at the same pace, rather than having to slow due to fatigue.

22 Muscular endurance is the ability to use the same muscle group repeatedly for a long period of time without tiring. It is important in tennis as it allows repeated contractions of the arm muscles to carry on striking the ball with pace and accuracy. Speed can relate to the whole body or a body part, and it relates to the quickness of a movement. It is important in tennis to move around the court: for example, chasing a drop shot if you are at the back of the court. Flexibility is the range of movement possible at a joint. This is important to the tennis player because it allows a better range of movement at the joint, so the player can generate more power when striking the ball, making it harder for the opponent to return. As seen, all three components are important and can offer some advantage to the player – if they lacked any of these components they would not be able to play as well, the quality of their play would drop, they would not have the pace to return a shot or would not be able to generate so much pace on the ball. However, without muscular endurance they would always lose the second or third set, therefore this must be the most important as without this their speed and power would be irrelevant as they would already be out of the match. Provided they had average flexibility, speed would probably be more of an asset, as their opponent will be trying to place the ball away from them and they will need to be quick to get to it.

127. Timed test 2

Note: These are sample answers, other responses are also possible.

1 (a) **C** It can be achieved by becoming better at sport.
  (b) **B** design, develop, monitor, evaluate
  (c) **A** overweight
  (d) **C** golf swing
  (e) **D** Complete the 800 m 1 second faster.
  (f) **B** clapping the opponent when they make an error

2 Reduced risk of stroke due to an improvement in cardiovascular fitness as an increase in CV fitness will mean regular aerobic training; this will reduce cholesterol, therefore lowering blood pressure and reducing the risk of a stroke.

3 (a) emotional; depression;
  (b) co-operation; social.

4 Serotonin gives a 'feel good' factor. Increased levels are released during physical activity, so if you are enjoying physical activity due to increased serotonin you are more likely to want to participate.

5 It is possible to under eat, i.e. to eat less than the recommended daily amount. If you do you will lose weight. If you continue to do this you will become underweight and eventually could become anorexic.

6 (a) Smoking causes a reduction in oxygen carrying capacity of the blood therefore impacting on the ability to exercise for a long time reducing cardiovascular fitness.
  (b) Bronchitis and emphysema

7 (a) The graph shows that the more physical activity you do, the lower the risk of disease; the less you do, the greater the risk of disease.
  (b) One of the risks associated with a sedentary lifestyle is obesity.

8 (a) Macronutrients: fats; carbohydrates; protein
    Micronutrients: vitamins; minerals
    Not placed: Water; fibre

  (b) Without a balanced diet containing carbohydrates you would not have the energy for exercise. By making sure you have energy to regularly exercise you will improve your health as you will be less likely to suffer from high blood pressure, so there will be less chance of coronary heart disease. With good health you should be well enough to exercise.

9 (a) So that the coach can design an appropriate practice.
  (b) Open–closed
  (c) A vault in gymnastics is a closed skill because the gymnast practices the skill over and over and then executes it exactly the same as they practised it, so the conditions remain stable.

10 **Age** As people get older they get more responsibility: for example, a full-time job. They may need to travel to work, reducing their free time even more. Therefore they may not participate as much as when they were younger due to having less free time.
  Gender This can impact on the type of sport you play. Some activities tend to be more socially acceptable for each gender: for example, fewer men will opt for dance and fewer women for rugby.

11 The sports company wants to make a profit selling its merchandise therefore it will use well-known sports personalities to advertise the things it wants to sell. The sports personalities' fans will want to buy these products, increasing sales for the sponsor. The companies pay so much to make sure the sports stars agree to work with them and not another company.

12 In 1980 there were no reported cases of the use of performance-enhancing drugs, although the number of drugs tests conducted that year was also low, the lowest number in fact for any of the years. Numbers of doping cases have been relatively low throughout, but the last three Olympics have seen an increase. For example, in 2004 there were 26 reported cases compared to 11 in 2000, although more people were tested in 2004 than any year previously. In 2008 even more people were tested but there was a drop in those testing positive. This trend continued in 2012, with the highest number of athletes ever tested but with the 6th lowest number of athletes being found positive for taking performance-enhancing drugs. This implies trends of increased numbers of tests but drop in numbers being found positive.

13 The girls are talking to each other so have a social network, which will help their social health. They seem to be having fun so this will also be a positive influence on their emotional health. However, in the image they are just sitting chatting rather than taking part in a more active pastime such as sport, so they will need to make sure they include some of this in their daily lives if they are to avoid a sedentary lifestyle. This could lead to all sorts of physical health issues such as obesity, especially if they drink a lot of alcohol (you can see they drink some from the image) due to the additional calories in alcohol, which could also lead to high blood pressure and increased cholesterol. In addition to the weight implication of drinking alcohol there are also other hazards: for example, kidney and liver damage, which could both cause long-term poor health. Similarly the girls are smoking. Smoking any number of cigarettes a day is said to increase the risk of lung cancer, so although the girls look happy in the picture and are clearly friends their lifestyle choices do not paint a very good picture in terms of their long-term physical health.

14 You can see that the game involves different types of skill. I would classify most of the skills as open as the game is played against opposition, although in the last image of the shooter they are shooting unopposed, therefore this is a much more closed skill. The closed skills would need to be developed in a different way to the open skills so that the skill practice sessions matched the requirements of the use of the skill in the activity. There are four different types of practice: massed or distributed, fixed or variable. Each type of practice is better for a particular classification of skill. Some of the different

skills in the images would be better taught in fixed practice conditions. This is because the situations do not change so the basketball player can learn to perfect the skill of shooting from the free throw line. If they were skilful and fit enough they could do this through massed practice, which would also be good because the player would experience fatigue during practice, as they will do in the game when they have to shoot. The rest of the skills would be developed through variable practice, as they are open skills that will need adapting when they are performed due to the presence of opponents. Once the skill has been learned, probably through distributed practice initially to allow the performer the chance for feedback between attempts to complete the skill, it could be further developed through variable practice, so the players will learn to vary how they perform the skills, adapting them as necessary, which they will have to do in their game.

Published by Pearson Education Limited, 80 Strand, London, WC2R 0RL.

www.pearsonschoolsandfecolleges.co.uk

Copies of official specifications for all Pearson qualifications may be found on the website: qualifications.pearson.com

Text and illustrations © Pearson Education Limited 2016
Typeset and illustrations by Kamae Design, Oxford
Produced by Cambridge Publishing Management Ltd
Cover illustration by Miriam Sturdee

The right of Jan Simister to be identified as author of this work has been asserted by her in accordance with the Copyright, Designs and Patents Act 1988.

First published 2016

19 18
10 9 8 7 6 5 4 3

British Library Cataloguing in Publication Data
A catalogue record for this book is available from the British Library

ISBN 9781292135083

Printed in Italy by L.E.G.O. S.p.A. Lavis (TN)

Acknowledgements
The author and publisher would like to thank the following individuals and organisations for permission to reproduce photographs:

Alamy Images: 81, John FryeR 66tc, Ingram Publishing 39t, sportpoint 6bl, Tetra Images 4r; **Fotolia.com:** Brenda Carson 122t; **Getty Images:** Emmanuel Dunand 109, Julian Finney 112, Stu Forster 37l, Paul Gilham 6tr, Hindustan Times 1b, Morne de Klerk 5br, Christof Koepsel 5tl, Matthew Lewis 6br, Dean Mouhtaropoulos 1t, Dan Mullan 123, Mike Powell 10, 11, simon2579 101, Jochen Tack 85, Murat Taner 66b; **Imagestate Media:** John Foxx Collection 45; **Pearson Education Ltd:** Tudor Photography 133t; **PhotoDisc:** Jules Frazier. 111, Photolink 97, 133br; **Photolibrary.com:** 14tl; **Shutterstock.com:** 38l, 66bc, 83, 87, Alexander Y 6tl, Diego Barbieri 30b, Peter Bernik 27, bikeriderlondon 21, 96, Aitor Bouzo Ateca 28, Chen Ws 40tr, Valentyna Chukhlyebova 3b, CLS Design 7b, Corepics VOF 60cr, decade3d - anatomy online 9b, Dim Dimich 2br, Neo Edmund 3c, emran 4l, Aurelie Fieschi 2t, Chris Hellyar 12t, Ipatov 13b, Robert J. Beyers II. 36, Sebastian Kaulitzki 2bc (r), Laszlo66 39b, Lilyana Vynogradova 122, John Lumb. 38r, Blazej Lyjak 14tr, maga 60l, Maxisport 12b, 40tl, Maya2008 2bc (l), Stephen Mcsweeny 125l, meunierd 60cl, Monkey Business Images. 133bl, Jim Noetzel 66t, NotarYES 37r, Mirenska Olga 5tr, oliveromg. 86, Monika Olszewska 5bl, Perspectives - Jeff Smith 60r, Sergey Peterman 43, Catalin Petolea 34, 127, Alexander Raths 133bc, Randall Reed 13t, Pete Saloutos 125r, Ljupco Smokovski 9t, stihii 2bl, testing 30t, Undrey 102, Krivosheev Vitaly. 40b, wavebreakmedia 15

All other images © Pearson Education

We are grateful to the following for permission to reproduce copyright material:

Graphs
Graphs on page 88 from CHILDREN'S BMI, OVERWEIGHT AND OBESITY, Health Survey for England - 2013 Vol 1, Chapter 11, fig 11b, page6 (Gary Boodhna), The Health and Social Care Information Centre HSCIC

Tables
Table on page 105 from https://www.sportengland.org/media/162187/01_1x30_overall_factsheet_aps7q2-final.pdf, Sport England; Figure 1 on page 106, Figure 1on page 107 from http://www.sportengland.org/media/913623/aps9q2headlines.pdf; Table on page 108 from Broadcast Viewing Levels Cumulative Audience **** (billion), Olympic-Marketing-Fact-File-2016.pdf, pp21; Figure on page 130 from Evidence on the impact of physical activity and its relationship to health, At least five a week. A report from the Chief Medical Officer, Gateway Ref: 2389, p17 (Department of Health, Physical Activity, Health Improvement and Prevention); Table on page 132 from The Fight Against Doping and Promotion of Athletes' Health, Jan 2010, International Olympic Committee's (IOC's) report, pp2

Text
Extract on page 109 from http://stakeholders.ofcom.org.uk/binaries/consultations/london2012/media-consumption/report.pdf

Notes from the publisher
1.
In order to ensure that this resource offers high-quality support for the associated Pearson qualification, it has been through a review process by the awarding body. This process confirms that this resource fully covers the teaching and learning content of the specification or part of a specification at which it is aimed. It also confirms that it demonstrates an appropriate balance between the development of subject skills, knowledge and understanding, in addition to preparation for assessment.

Endorsement does not cover any guidance on assessment activities or processes (e.g. practice questions or advice on how to answer assessment questions), included in the resource nor does it prescribe any particular approach to the teaching or delivery of a related course.

While the publishers have made every attempt to ensure that advice on the qualification and its assessment is accurate, the official specification and associated assessment guidance materials are the only authoritative source of information and should always be referred to for definitive guidance.

Pearson examiners have not contributed to any sections in this resource relevant to examination papers for which they have responsibility.

Examiners will not use endorsed resources as a source of material for any assessment set by Pearson.

Endorsement of a resource does not mean that the resource is required to achieve this Pearson qualification, nor does it mean that it is the only suitable material available to support the qualification, and any resource lists produced by the awarding body shall include this and other appropriate resources.

2.
Pearson has robust editorial processes, including answer and fact checks, to ensure the accuracy of the content in this publication, and every effort is made to ensure this publication is free of errors. We are, however, only human, and occasionally errors do occur. Pearson is not liable for any misunderstandings that arise as a result of errors in this publication, but it is our priority to ensure that the content is accurate. If you spot an error, please do contact us at resourcescorrections@pearson.com so we can make sure it is corrected.